PRISONERS OF METH
Imprisoned and Turned Upside Down

By

Jesse W. Hambrick Jr.

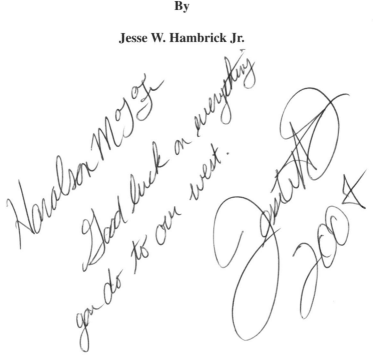

Self published in the United States by Jesse W. Hambrick

Hambrick, Jesse W.
Prisoners of Meth: Imprisoned and Turned Upside Down /
Jesse W. Hambrick Jr.

Library of Congress Catalog Number: **TXu-1-258-169**
ISBN: 1-59971-887-1

For more information or to order books, please visit
www.prisonersofmeth.com

Printed by
Appleby & Associates
770.944.0452

Dedication

Prisoners of Meth, is dedicated to my beautiful wife, Laurie, our three great children, and my family who have all supported me in this endeavor. Without their constant love and support I would never be where I am now.

Jesse W. Hambrick Jr.

Special Thanks

The author would like to thank the following people that were so important in making this book a reality. Without these people this book would not be in the hands of the people that need it the most; prisoners of Meth. Each person has given me a piece of the puzzle that was needed to put this book together. Thank you for your support of me in this endeavor.

Natalie Bentley
Sam and Charmaine Marlow
Amy Talley
Penny Lenormand
Sheriff Phil Miller
Chief Stan Copeland
Douglas County Sheriff's Office Special Investigations Division
Douglas County Meth Task Force
Jesse W. Hambrick Sr.
Chinita Hayden
Charles and Mildred Clonts
Every person in recovery that helped me better understand the dangers of Meth and how to help those that need help.
Thanks to our Lord and Savior Jesus Christ who gave us the original example of love and sacrifice to our fellow man.

Table of Contents

Preface

Methamphetamine imprisons its users in addiction and it has the power to sentence them to a life of heartache that may not know an end. An even sadder truth is that many family members and friends of those dealing with a Meth addiction are sentenced right along side their loved one to a life filled with misery and heartache. They must hopelessly stand by and watch their loved one fall into a spiral of destruction. Those hopeless people are the children that are forced to live with Meth addicted parents, or it might be a husband or wife that has to watch their spouse leave everything they have worked for to run the streets of addiction. It might also be the grandparent who is now raising a grandchild as their own not knowing where they went wrong in raising their own child. Many of the same symptoms that are discussed in this book that plague Methamphetamine users are shared by the ones around them that love them the most. The fact is though that the loved ones don't have the drug to numb their senses while they deal with the depression, stress, and anger resulting from Methamphetamine abuse. They, even more than the addict themselves, realize that they are prisoners of Meth.

This book was written to help those people that are looking for answers, find those answers through a better understanding of Meth addiction. This text attempts to explain what Meth is through its street names, origins, description, and the effects that it has on the user. The book also identifies the ABCs of how to intervene in the life of an addict that does not want help. The book also contains pages in the back for note taking as you begin to develop a plan. In essence, this workbook revolves around getting the person you love the help they need, but often do not want.

Jesse W. Hambrick Jr.

Introduction

I was speaking at a PTA meeting one evening at a local middle school as I had done many times in the past. I was giving a Methamphetamine awareness class to several hundred local parents and had just concluded the speech when a stranger walked up and introduced himself to me. After talking for several minutes, he made a comment that has stuck with me ever since. He said, "Methamphetamine makes you love the people you hate and hate the people you love."

This statement came from someone that I had something in common with and that I would eventually call a friend. He was someone that hated Methamphetamine like I did, but knew it from a slightly different angle. It was from the angle probably most feared – from that of a parent who had a son addicted to Methamphetamine.

His comment surmised what I knew all too well and it also allowed me to see the drug from a different point of view. It came from someone that you wouldn't normally think that I could call a friend; someone that might have typically hated me.

When I said that he approached me that day, I purposely did not tell you how he introduced himself. He was the father of a boy that I had arrested and jailed for being in possession of Methamphetamine. I had not just put him in jail once, but twice. Usually this type of introduction is one followed by angry comments or a lashing out from the parent, but on this particular day I was met with handshakes and genuine appreciation.

He explained that his son had thrown away so many things after becoming addicted to Methamphetamine. He had his good looks, a beautiful wife and daughter, a promising job, a respected family name and a Christian upbringing. These should have been enough of a reason to have been on the straight and narrow, but instead he was lost on a dark and winding path.

His parents had so many questions about what had gone wrong and came to this PTA meeting in search of answers. They became desperate enough to attend this meeting where they knew I would be speaking and planned to reach out to me to find answers. I may have been the investigator that had arrested their son, but in time they would call me their friend.

Since that first meeting, they have thanked me several more times for saving their son's life and have become active in spreading the word about the dangers of Methamphetamine, and since that first meeting, we worked together to get their son out of jail and into treatment – hopefully both for the last time.

Just prior to writing this book, I began developing friendships like the one I just described with many different people. Moreover, it seemed that everywhere I turned there was someone looking for help with a child, friend or parent that was addicted to Methamphetamine.

In fact, as I was typing the previous paragraph, I had to stop and take a call from the mother of a 33 year old woman who just admitted to her that she has been using the drug for three years. This was a story I had become accustomed to hearing on a regular basis. She explained that her daughter had lost her job, her house and was in the process of signing her three children over to "grandma's" care. The desire to write this book came about as a result of those many calls that revealed these tragic stories and from those friendships that forged under the worst circumstances.

If you are reading this book, you are probably in search of more information on Methamphetamine in general or, even more likely, are looking for a way to help someone dear to you that is fighting and struggling with addiction. For every person addicted to Methamphetamine, there are many more people around them that are just as affected. These people parents, children, friends, spouses, siblings literally experience a misery all of their own. I understand that.

I want this to be a guide for you to be able to gain focus and begin doing something about the problem you are facing. In this book, I will tell you about myself and how I became involved with Methamphetamine through my career. I will also explain what Methamphetamine is and how it affects those using the drug. I will give you the signs and symptoms of Methamphetamine use so that you can be reasonably sure that there is a problem. And lastly, I'll help you devise a plan to intervene in the life of the addicted person and assist you in putting that plan of action into place.

I want you to break free from the helpless prison that you are in and, by helping your loved one with their Methamphetamine addiction, be able to turn your life and theirs right side up again.

Methamphetamine in My Life

I knew from the time I was a small boy that I wanted to be in law enforcement. Well, actually I wanted to be an Air Force pilot flying fighter jets, but a color vision problem kept me on the ground. Little did I know then that if I had been able to go on as a pilot, I would have served in two wars and probably not have had the chance to write this book.

Now I don't want you to think that I just settled on being a policeman. I was actually just as interested in a career as a law enforcement officer as I was a career flying. I have a drawing that I sketched when I was about five years old in my office. It is a picture of me in a police car chasing what I think was meant to be bank robbers. I guess even then I knew that in one way or another I wanted to be a "good guy" chasing down the "bad guys."

This stuck with me throughout my childhood and teenage years and I always seemed to be the one standing up for what was right just because it was right. I was raised in a Christian home and in a Christian school, but I will admit that I had a devious side as well. I never experimented with drugs because I knew it was wrong, but I did have my fair share of trouble and even a few minor scrapes with the local police. I had friends that smoked pot and one that was rumored to use cocaine, but in Smyrna, Georgia and during the late 80's, drugs weren't a major concern for the kids or for their parents. I guess I always felt that I wanted to make a difference and that police work would be a good way to do this.

As soon as I graduated high school, I started my career in law enforcement by getting my foot in the door as a radio operator for a local police department. I spent some time working in the radio room and then went to work for a Metro Atlanta sheriff's office in the jail. It wasn't until 1994 that I began working the streets as a patrol officer. It was in this capacity that I started to have major interactions with drugs and drug use. Up until that point, I had no real involvement with illegal drugs of any kind, personal or work related. But after that point, I had my fair share of dealing with people using marijuana and crack cocaine.

We had an area in the city that was called "The Crack" where I would make several drug arrests each week. The crack was a small community made up of two dead end streets that were well known throughout the Atlanta area as the place to buy crack cocaine in an open air market. I took it really personally that these dealers were peddling crack cocaine in my city and in such a flagrant manner. As I worked making drug arrests, it didn't take long before I realized that this was an area that I could devote my attention to and simultaneously make a big difference.

Even more than any other type of crime, it seemed that the people that used illegal narcotics were in a world of their own. I wanted to get inside that world and find out more. Of course at that time my only interest was in putting the bad guys away for a long time. I didn't want to hear the words rehabilitation or treatment. I only wanted to see seizures, arrests and prison sentences. Even though I had such an interest in narcotics, I had never considered working as a full time narcotics officer.

I remember very clearly the day that would forever change my career. It was a Saturday, and I was working around the house (dressed for painting) and doing other mundane weekend chores. Halfway through the day, I got a call from my Chief of Police. True to form, he got right to the point and asked me, "Have you every thought about working dope?" I told him that I hadn't really considered it before and he said that I should. I told him that I would consider the opportunity and he came back with, "Good, come to the station and take a polygraph to see if you can be assigned to the task force."

At that time I didn't even know what the task force was. On the way to the police department, I started having images of all the television shows that I had watched growing up. I day dreamed about what I thought a job on the task force would be like. I said to myself, "I get to let my hair grow out, set my own schedule, and not wear a uniform anymore. Man, this job could have it perks."

When I arrived at the police department, I took my polygraph exam and passed with no problem. By the end of that afternoon, I had been assigned to the multi-county drug task force. Of course it wasn't until I was on my way home that I remembered that I hadn't even discussed this with my wife.

My wife was not happy at all, and she turned out to not be very supportive of my move. My career choice along with my young age contributed to our divorce. I continued in my career and I, in turn, did exactly what I thought I would do. I let my hair grow long, worked my own schedule and very rarely put on a uniform. I was good at what I did though.

Working as a narcotics officer felt natural to me. I was quick on my feet, smart and motivated to put people in jail for drug violations. I spent almost six years working in that assignment and loved every minute.

During that time, I handled every type of case imaginable. I did things that I saw on television and lived life by the seat of my pants. I worked both large and small investigations revolving around marijuana, cocaine, crack cocaine and even an occasional LSD or ecstasy case. I always loved working the Methamphetamine cases though.

These people were a different kind of drug user. They were usually smart about dealing drugs (if there is such a thing), but they also had a side to them that made them extremely unpredictable. They were organized and well prepared even though they were so volatile. On one particular case, I spent months working myself into a group that netted a bust of multiple pounds of Methamphetamine and sent numerous suspects to federal prison. Even then, Methamphetamine was still just another drug and arresting people involved with it was all I was interested in.

It was also during this time that I started developing a taste for teaching. I enjoyed telling others about the dangers of drugs and keeping other officers up to date on the latest trends and newest case laws. I began speaking in some of the local schools during red ribbon week, teaching the children the dangers of marijuana, cocaine and Methamphetamine.

Completely by accident I began doing more and more of these "drug talks" – mainly because everyone else in the unit adamantly refused to do them. As you can imagine, public speaking is not something that most policeman want to do, given their charming personality and easy going demeanor. I didn't mind handling the calls from someone requesting another "drug talk." For me, these talks were just another way to divert people from drugs so I wouldn't have to fight, chase or get into a gun battle with them later in life. I didn't realize it then, but it was my first taste of a big word that I didn't care much for – PREVENTION.

The next major directional change in my career was when I had a co-worker and friend die in the line of duty. Robbie worked on the interstate conducting what we "highway interdiction." This meant that his primary purpose was to identify people transporting bulk quantities of illegal drugs over the interstates. I had known Robbie for a couple years and was often the narcotics investigator that followed up on his seizures and arrests. This gave me the opportunity to work cases that were on a larger level that many local law enforcement officers might never get a chance to do. I developed a solid working knowledge of the techniques that these major drug dealer techniques utilized while they peddled thousands of pounds of illegal narcotics all over the United States. Robbie and I became close and even spent some time together outside the office. On the day that he was killed, I was working close by. I had no idea, nor considered it a possibility, that one of our own could die. Who would have known that a small time criminal from New York would kill Robbie that day?

I responded to the scene and watched the medics load him into the ambulance and drive away. I would not see Robbie alive again. During the days that followed, I couldn't make sense of why he died or why he even allowed himself to get into that situation. This struck me hard in both my head and my heart. When you lose someone close to you like that, you often reconsider your choice of careers, "Is this worth it? Is fighting crime and giving so much of myself worth the risk of being murdered just because of what I do?"

I asked myself if I died in the line of duty would my family care how many people I arrested or how many pounds of drugs or illegal money I had seized. At this point, I almost quit working narcotics entirely. However, I slowly began to realize that although I was making a small difference, it was a difference that would not matter very much after I was gone.

In 2000, I left where I was working and thought I was going to get out of narcotics work all together. I began focusing more on teaching and wanted to put to good use all the vast knowledge I had gained in the area of illegal narcotics. I went back to patrol for several months and was completely unhappy because I missed the work. I also realized that I had developed a strong aversion to polyester uniforms and wanted back into the underworld of drugs. So, out of an act of desperation I decided to try D.A.R.E. (Drug Awareness and Resistance Education) on for size.

Most of you know that D.A.R.E. is a program designed to educate children on reasons why they should not do drugs. This was a great program and the course to become a certified D.A.R.E. instructor was one of the toughest law enforcement classes I had ever been through. I will admit the course was something completely new to me. It was based on good feelings and caring instead of the bad feelings, hate, and coldness of being a narcotics officer. I felt a bit out of place with this, but it felt good to take a new approach to an old problem. Although I did not know it, this was my first experience with another word I wasn't used to – EDUCATION.

It didn't take long to realize that I wasn't cut out to be a teacher working in the public school system. I did however develop a healthy respect for teachers out there doing their job day in and day out. I couldn't seem to get comfortable and find my niche teaching kids, many of those kids whom didn't care to learn. I was a hardened law enforcement officer in a world where I couldn't employ all the tactics I learned over the better part of a decade. I decided to leave the D.A.R.E. program. So yet again, I headed back to the underworld of narcotics back to my career home.

Things hadn't changed all that much during my hiatus. What did change though was a new drug that was sneaking up on everyone. There was a fascination I had with this drug from the very beginning. It was potent, addictive and looked like kid's candy. Its street name was ICE. It was like something you would see in movies set in some futuristic place where this cool looking drug was taking over the world. The problem was that this wasn't the future and this drug was a real threat to the community. I was looking for a fresh approach to working as a narcotics investigator and maybe this was where I would wage my battle. Little did I know that this was not going to be just a battle; it was going to turn into a war.

My first experience with a person reaching out for help was from a mother who had a 16 year-old daughter that was addicted to cocaine, heroin and ICE. The young girl had stolen her mother's credit card and disappeared into the darkness of the drug world in an attempt to never be seen again. This was after she had just been arrested and her mother bonded her out of jail thinking that she had learned a lesson. We had pressed her mother not to get her out, but she didn't listen and did what many parent think they should do.

Working with this mother was truly inspirational. She was not about to lie down and let her daughter die. She became the one man mom squad and went on the hunt for her daughter. She turned over every rock and looked in every corner and fed all the information she could to me and my partner. After several weeks, she emerged with her daughter in tow leaving behind a wake of arrests, drug seizures and drug dealers running scared. Her story would be a book in and of itself.

Over the next several months we joined forces to keep her daughter clean. I was able to interview her and got a lengthy video with her daughter concerning her drug use. She was the first of many addicts that began teaching me another side to Methamphetamine. I slowly began to realize that there was much more of a story to these people than just stats and information on local drug dealers. I began to see them as real people with a problem, and not just looking at them as the problem.

Over the course of the next two years, I watched this young girl get arrested six times for various offenses revolving around her use in illegal narcotics. I knew that something wasn't working. Being in and out of jail and having at least one near death experience was not stopping her use. There had to be more. I didn't know it, but I was dabbling in an area that was a bad word to most narcotics officers – TREATMENT.

During 2003, I started dealing with more and more parents in the same situation and became an unofficial counselor to parents, friends and family members that were willing to fight to help someone get off Methamphetamine. To my co-workers, I became the bleeding heart of the unit. I saw a huge need and even considered mentioning the idea of forming a community group against Methamphetamine to my superiors. Throughout the year, that idea stayed in the back of my mind where it was safe and would not cause anymore "bleeding heart" comments at work.

That entire time, I was building a knowledge base of treatment options, perfecting my teaching presentations and increasing my clinical knowledge of the monster known as ICE. I began teaching classes to other law enforcement officers on various drugs including Methamphetamine, continued interventions and made arrest after arrest for possession, distribution and manufacturing. I went to Washington, D.C. to become certified on how to investigate and dismantle clandestine Methamphetamine labs and was the first person in my county to receive this certification. This class further fueled my interest because now I knew even more about the drug and how easily it was made.

It seemed that all the other drugs were taking a back seat to Methamphetamine and the type of person using it was changing. I began to see younger and younger kids using it and those that you wouldn't think would take drugs in the first place. As a general rule, kids that are involved at home, with sports, in church and with a good friend base are less likely to use drugs than those that don't have one or all those things. That was not true with Methamphetamine.

The kids that were ending up strung out on this stuff were in school with good grades, both parents at home and a whole lot of friends that were headed in the right direction. So many more young girls were ending up on it – and I began to see my daughters' faces in each one of theirs. I prayed for a way to make a difference in this war and sat back and waited for my time to take action.

In January of 2004, I had the great fortune of meeting Dr. Vance Boddy, a local doctor in our area. He too, had been seeing the difference in his family practice and was tired of treating teenage Methamphetamine addicts. He approached my Sheriff and asked if there was anything that could be done. Of course at that time my name had become synonymous with the word Methamphetamine, so the Sheriff put me in touch with Dr. Boddy. This meeting was the final push that I needed.

After only a few minutes, we decided to create a community task force whose sole purpose was fighting Methamphetamine use and abuse. Less than a month after that, the Douglas County Methamphetamine Task Force, or DCMTF, was launched. It was the first of its kind in the state of Georgia, and became my primary platform to not only fight, but to enlist my community.

DCMTF was created to unite the community in an effort to combat Methamphetamine and its production in Douglas County. The task force is comprised of approximately 25 members and includes the like of local treatment providers, state and local family protective services, local fire and law enforcement personnel, board of education members, the Juvenile Court Judge, the Chief District Attorney and others dedicated to the war on Meth. The objective was to attack the Methamphetamine abuse on a four prong approach: treatment, education, prevention and enforcement. A committee was formed for each, with specific goals outlined for a designated approach. This strategy not only targeted areas of need, but also united the community's resources to better combat and treat the problem.

The Treatment Committee was made up of several local providers that offered a vast array of options, consisting of court mandated treatment (both in and out of custody), as well as long term treatment for those seeking help on a voluntary basis. This enabled those with a Methamphetamine addiction to seek treatment before the police intervened. The task force stood behind the theory that Methamphetamine users and addicts need treatment. These programs also offered a wide range of support programs for family members of addicts.

The Education Committee was geared toward educating those persons that were not at risk for Methamphetamine use, but because of their work or personal involvement, needed to be educated on the drug and the dangers it posed. The task force was involved in training law enforcement, state employees, crisis shelter employees, public educators and a host of others that had requested training on Meth and Meth labs.

The training consisted of information that would help the student understand the drug through it origins, appearance, and the effects on the user. We also described how to identify a Meth lab and how to respond to that discovery. Through this, we also participated in developing protocols for state and local DFACS (Department of Family and Children Services) workers on drug endangered children (DEC).

The Prevention Committee focused its efforts on those persons that were at risk for using Methamphetamine. This group was involved in developing and distributing brochures and fliers on the effects of the drug and the labs needed to produce it. The committee also acted as the public awareness arm of the task force and participated in local awareness through the task force web site (www.meth-in-douglas.com) as well as other grassroots initiatives.

The Enforcement Committee was geared toward the investigation and arrest of those persons that were involved in Meth production or distribution. The task force web site and tip line were instrumental in offering local community members an avenue to report crime anonymously through an email and phone system that were monitored by the task force. This information was used by the Douglas County Sheriff's Office to identify and arrest Meth violators. This committee had also combined efforts with the ATF in addressing the increase in weapons and explosives possessed by Methamphetamine addicts and producers. This allowed the team to seek federal prosecution for producers and distributors.

I can't even tell you all the accomplishments we had in just one year's time, but it propelled me into a full time bleeding heart position. The task force was based on all that I had learned in the 10 years of narcotics enforcement: prevention, education, treatment and enforcement. As a group, we truly began to make a difference in the lives of people dealing with a Methamphetamine problem.

I continued teaching during the latter part of 2004 all over the southeast and by the time this book was being written I had taught and educated some 10,000 people on the Methamphetamine epidemic. The missing link was that I still had not satisfied my original desire to help people help someone addicted to Meth. I still had so many people that were coming to me and describing the prison that they were in, the helpless feelings that they were having and the way that their lives had been turned upside down by their loved ones being addicted to Meth. These people were not using or addicted to Methamphetamine, but had become a prisoner just the same.

I can't explain the number of tragic stories that I had to listen to about the college graduates, doctors, lawyers, drug counselors and others that had fallen prey to the drug. I guess these encounters, more than anything, led me to consider starting a support group for parents, family members, and friends of Methamphetamine addicts. Many of those parents, family and friends of Methamphetamine addicts are who asked me to write a book to help the millions of people that needed help in helping others. The following pages are based on the support group that I envisioned and was started here in my community as a result of that vision, and maybe, just maybe, it can help you in finding the answers you search for.

In the next few chapters, I want to give you the plain English understanding of what Methamphetamine is. I want you to have a basic understanding of the drug through its affects on the brain, its origins and the signs and symptoms of its use. I am not a doctor, I am not a treatment specialist, and I am not a lawyer, but I am someone with extensive knowledge in the first hand practical experience in dealing with these users day in and day out for years. Many doctors, lawyers, and treatment specialist have sat in on my training for a better working knowledge of Methamphetamine.

Common Street Names

Methamphetamine is a drug that has more street names that are used in describing it than any other drug that I have seen. Literally there are hundreds of street names for Methamphetamine, but some of the more favorite are ICE, crystal, speed, crank, glass, shards, Tina and go fast. Methamphetamine gets its street names in several different ways, but the most prevalent ways are from three main areas. It gets its nicknames from the way it makes you act, the way it looks, or from something borrowed from regular life.

Methamphetamine is called speed, go fast or go juice because those people that are on it are usually going a hundred miles an hour. Methamphetamine is called glass, crystal or ICE because it often looks like tiny pieces of glass or rock candy. And lastly, it is often called "crystal light" because it can be stirred into a drink for ingestion. I've heard it referred to as "crankenstein" because it makes a monster out of you. It might also be called the "Jenny crank diet" because it causes you to often lose dramatic amounts of weight.

The scary thing is that many users start using Methamphetamine not knowing that they're using it because it was introduced to them as something else like speed or Tina. Many users have told me that they believed they were taking some new drug and not Meth. Had they known it was Methamphetamine, many said they would have never used it in the first place. Of course, there will always be new names that someone comes up with, so I suggest researching the internet to keep up with the latest street terms. You'll be surprised to hear someone talking about inviting "Tina" to the party or making sure there is plenty of "ICE" there for everyone to use. The bottom line, regardless of what you call the drug, is that it is designed to do one thing kill you.

Effects on the Body and Brain

Methamphetamine is recognized by anyone that knows anything about the drug as one of the most addictive substances known to man. My definition of addiction is the uncontrollable desire produced by the drug to make the user want more and more. This is caused by the user's need to experience the euphoria of the first time high or, longer term, to combat the wretched side effects once the addiction has taken over. Our society as a whole has lost sight of the meaning of the words "love" and "addiction".

Many users think that they can pick Methamphetamine up and then stop when the affect is not longer desired. If that was really the case, we would have a lot of people running around with Meth hobbies and not Meth habits. Methamphetamine is one of those instantaneously addictive drugs that causes an immediate need for more. Statistics say that you have a greater than ninety percent chance of using the drug a second and the instant addiction rate soars to greater than 25 percent. I personally have met only a handful of one time Meth users, so I agree completely with those statistics.

Let me explain to you in my own words how Methamphetamine affects the human body and why it is so addictive. Meth is a central nervous system stimulant or CNS. It directly affects the brain by causing it to overproduce many different chemicals, such as adrenaline and dopamine. The way that these two chemicals levels are affected by the drug explains why the users act as they do.

When adrenaline is released in our body, it causes the flight or fight response. We have all experienced it as part of our normal, everyday lives. Remember when you were a small child and you had to climb a set of stairs in the dark by yourself? The first few steps were fine, but the more steps you climbed the more you were convinced that someone was right on your heels. By the time that you reached the top of the staircase, it seemed as if your feet weren't even touching the ground. The more adrenaline released, the more scared you got and the faster you ran.

When Methamphetamine is introduced into the body, the brain is constantly "tweaked" by releases of adrenaline. The same as in the example of the small child, the users often become paranoid and feel as if they are being watched or followed. They often hide, run away or fight for no apparent reason at all to the people on the outside. For them however, these actions are completely justified.

Dopamine, on the other hand, is the neurotransmitter that allows us to sense pleasure. It is normally released in the brain in small amounts during enjoyable physical or mental contact. It is released and then recaptured the brain. It is not reproduced. If you destroy it, you can't get it back.

For example, during normal sexual interaction, dopamine is released to let us know that the actions we are engaged in are pleasurable. When the sexual behavior is ceased, the body begins to recollect the dopamine for use again later – and we eventually return to a normal state of mind. Sex and Methamphetamine go hand in hand. When a person uses it, they experience a release of dopamine that makes them feel more pleasure than we can understand. The problem is that your brain realizes that there is a problem and it sends out enzymes that destroy the free floating dopamine.

In plain English, that means that because the user is experiencing the constant rush of adrenaline they begin to develop symptoms of paranoia and schizophrenic type behavior. Also the depletion of dopamine means that the brain is no longer stimulated by the things that it used to find pleasure in before the person started using Meth. The drug actually begins replacing the desire for anything else other than the drug itself. The user no longer finds pleasure in normal sexual behavior, spending time with their family or with their children or anything else for that matter.

Methamphetamine is one of the few known substances that is strong enough to break the strongest human bond we have the bond between a mother and child. I have seen many mothers that are willing to give up their children because it interferes with their Meth use and can do it with no emotion or remorse. It's my sense that the depletion of dopamine has a tremendous amount to do with this.

For the longest time, I looked down on addicts and thought that there must be something wrong with them to have fallen prey to whatever drug it was that they were addicted to. Then I realized that our society has many addicts in one way or another. It is easy to understand a drug addiction when we look at ourselves and the way we act on a day to day basis.

For example, we are all in the search to feel good. We drink coffee, smoke cigarettes or do one of many other things to "get us going" in the morning and feeling normal. Now no one has died of a coffee addiction, but that small addiction often drives us to act in certain ways just the same. We all know someone that is miserable when they don't get their morning coffee. Imagine what you would do for a soda or coffee if you didn't have one. Have you ever woken up and felt the need for a soda or coffee? Most of us wouldn't kill or steal to have it, but at what length would we go to get it?

As we go throughout the remainder of the day, we usually experience many positive or good feelings. Generally there are three areas that we can associate with in our lives that give us an understanding of good physical or mental pleasure. They are sex, food and money. Think of all the things that people do to get themselves in trouble in these areas. Think how you might feel if you went to lunch and scratched a winning lottery ticket for a large sum of money. We would feel great and probably spend the rest of the day, week or our life not going back to work. I bet we could all think of something that we did regarding sex, food or money that wasn't our smartest move.

Of course we also deal with negative feelings and emotions like physical sickness, financial trouble or the death of a friend or family member. We try with all our strength to get out of the emotional lows that we have. Most of us would do just about anything to get out of what we're experiencing. People often turn to medicine, alcohol, drugs or some other activity to make them feel normal again. The same is true for that of a Methamphetamine addiction.

For one reason or another, a person decides to use Meth for the first time. Many times that decision is based on the pursuit of wanting to feel better or to get away from some negative emotion or trouble. For whatever the reason, they use the drug initially and experience a release of dopamine that makes them feel as if they were on top of the world. But, with every high, there is always a low, or what is often called "coming down."

The body experiences nausea, paranoia, rapid heart rate and other awful side effects. The easiest way to find that pleasure again and to combat that crashing feeling is to use more Meth. Because of the depletion of dopamine and the fact that the body begins to resist and tolerate the drug, the user can no longer find that first high. The body actually builds up an antibody and begins to resist the drug being introduced to the system. It is now impossible for the user to feel the pleasure of the first time high.

Many users often say they are constantly chasing this feeling. As the body is depleted of dopamine, the user finds themselves sinking further and further into the "bad" side of their physical and emotional wellbeing and actually needs to drug just to feel normal. The story of one young woman, who was a habitual user, demonstrates this hell so clearly.

She told me that she used Meth so much that she would be up for days driven by her need for the drug. After her binge, she would crash for hours and hours of catatonic like sleep. Her husband would have to take a small Visine bottle filled with hot water and dissolved Methamphetamine and inject the mixture into her rectum in order for her to even wake up and function.

This type situation shows the need that is created in the body for the drug in order for the user to function and feel normal. The user is no longer taking the drug to get the good feelings they once had, and often begin to resent their need for the drug to lead a normal life. Without it, they can not feel normal and will, in fact, always find themselves on the "bad" side of life.

The initial feelings of pleasure that users experience drive them to use Meth more and more. At the same time, they are also battling feeling the negative effects that begin as a result of their addiction. I hope that you're beginning to see the power that Methamphetamine can have on someone and why it is so difficult for them to let go. I hope you're beginning to see why they will choose Meth over the important things in their lives, including work, friends, family or even their own children.

Origins of the Drug

So where did Methamphetamine originally come from? Most people believe that it has only been around for a few years maybe a decade or two tops. In reality, Meth was created over 100 years ago. It was synthesized by a Japanese scientist in 1919. Its close relative, Amphetamine, has been around since a German scientist synthesized it in 1887.

I want to take a moment to explain the difference in Amphetamine and Methamphetamine from a street level perspective. The drugs are very similar on a chemical level, but the major difference is when you hear someone say Amphetamine, they are generally talking about a clinically produced and legally used drug. When you hear someone talking about Methamphetamine, they are generally referring to the illegally produced and used drug. Even urine test kits often do not distinguish the difference between the two and many times parents or family members are confused when a drug test comes back positive for Amphetamine instead of Meth. Because they are so closely related, the latter will synthesize into the previous drug after a period of time in the body.

Both Amphetamine and Methamphetamine have been an important part of our history since the mid 30s. During this time, Amphetamine was marketed under the name Benzedrine and was used to treat congestion. In the 40s, during the World Wars, Hitler was suspected of being an Amphetamine addict and he has been credited with creating the "Nazi" method of producing the drug. In addition to his use, Hitler also gave the drug to his soldiers, and it was also commonly used by the Japanese military as well.

I have read and researched stories of the Japanese kamikaze pilots injecting Methamphetamine to numb their fears and keep them awake as they took long flights on their mission to bomb Pearl Harbor. During the 50s, Benzedrine was used to treat disorders like obesity and depression in the United States. In 1954 Japan had already developed an epidemic problem with Methamphetamine. It is estimated that one in every forty people in Japan was addicted to Meth during this time.

In 1957, Americans began shooting up Benzedrine that was drawn from the inhalers. In 1970, the Controlled Substances Act was passed which restricted the access to it. Because the drug became harder to get legally, people figured out a way to make the drug illegally. That's when Meth labs started springing up on the West Coast. They were primarily controlled by the Outlaw motorcycle gangs and why the drug became known as the "white redneck drug" and "white man's cocaine."

In my investigations, it always proved true that the drug was being bought and sold by a white male ages 25 to 35. Between 1990 and 2005, the drug became controlled by Hispanic cartels motivated by profit. The fact that the drug had become less of a racial entity and began being sold strictly for profit made the market for the drug expand into every race. That is why we saw and increase in the number of African American and Hispanics both selling and using the drug on the east coast. Of course, in the late 90s we saw ICE Methamphetamine begin to sweep the country, with abuse at epidemic proportions. In 1999, there were an estimated nine million Meth users nationwide, and that was before it caught on in the east coast drug market. Today, it is believed that there could be as many as 15 million users nationwide.

Physical Descriptions and Ways of Ingestion

What does Methamphetamine look like? The question is one that many parents and loved ones have asked me over and over again. There are two types of Methamphetamine that are currently found in American society powder forms of Methamphetamine and ICE Methamphetamine.

Powder Methamphetamine is the original "old school" form of the drug and is usually referred to as Tina or Crank. It is most commonly snorted, but can also be swallowed or mixed into any liquid for drinking. Most commonly, it's found in a fine crystalline powder that looks like salt. It is often white or off-white, but I've also seen it in red, pink, brown and tan. The color is a direct correlation to the chemicals left behind in the manufacturing process.

The other type Methamphetamine is known as ICE Methamphetamine. In Georgia and throughout the Southeast United States, this version makes up the majority of what is sold and used. ICE looks like rock salt or rock candy. It is a larger crystal and is often clear to cloudy opaque in color. The crystals can be very large and are referred to as shards. ICE is much more potent than its powder form counterpart. And because it can be smoked, it is much more addictive.

Any drug that can be smoked is more effectively used by the body than any other way of introducing a drug to our system, matched only by IV introduction to the body. That is why ICE Methamphetamine and crack cocaine are often referred to as "instantaneously addictive" drugs. The major difference in ICE and crack cocaine is that crack cocaine is not water soluble and can only be smoked.

On the other hand, ICE is a hydrochloride and can be easily dissolved in water. This means that you can introduce Methamphetamine into the system in many different ways. You can inject, smoke, snort or eat ICE. There is even a way of ingestion that is referred to as hot railing. (That's when a user heats a glass pipe until it is glowing red and then snorts a line of the drug, causing it to vaporize and be ingested through the nose as a vapor.)

The unusual thing about the way you use Meth is that each way to ingest it produces a different high. Snorting it gives the user the increased energy with little euphoric type feelings. Smoking it causes the euphoric type feelings. Shooting it causes the user to shut down in a trance like state caused by the senses being sped up beyond function. A young woman told me once that when you shoot up Methamphetamine, you have to sit still because if you moved, everything would be in fast forward. Because of the many type highs the drug becomes even more desirable to users.

Signs of Use

I think the most important part of this book is this chapter which is dedicated to the indicators of Methamphetamine use. The signs of use are very difficult to hide. The thing to remember though is that not all these symptoms are present in every user and not every user shows every sign. However, a user will, without fail, show some signs of use. As we cover each sign, make a mental check if the person you are thinking about is showing the symptom. If you have several of these marks, then there is probably a good reason for alarm.

Irritability and aggressive behavior are both two prevalent indicators. If you talk to anyone that has lived with a Methamphetamine addict for any length of time they will often refer to their loved ones as "down right mean" while that person is using. Like a child, Meth users become irritable and aggressive when they don't get what they want, the drug. When they don't have access to it, they have a hard time feeling normal and experience symptoms that cause them to act cranky.

If you are seeing constant mood swings throughout the course of the day or week you may seeing the first symptom of Methamphetamine use. People that are very lethargic at one point of the day and then full of excessive energy a short time later may be displaying symptoms of Meth use. Many users are short tempered and hard to get along with during their use. Children are often a victim of this symptom because the parent or user has no tolerance for the normal stress that goes along with child rearing. Typically, users are only thinking about one thing their next high. Anything that takes away from that, like caring for a child, is a nuisance and results in aggressive behavior. Understandably, domestic violence is increased as a result of this agitation as users become more prone to arguing or fights.

A conversation that I had with a Meth cooker led me to understand how even this minor indicator can lead to major problems. The cook told me that she and her husband were addicted and, as a result, began making the drug in their basement and shed. She told me that before they started using Methamphetamine, they had a story book relationship in which they never had a fight prior to their use. She said that on the day they were arrested, they were screaming and fighting with one another. That fight led them inside and away from the cook that they were working on. Shortly after, their shed caught on fire and rescue workers arrived at the scene. Needless to say, once the local sheriff's office responded, they were both arrested for producing Meth.

Anxiety, stress and nervousness are often signs that are a result of the moral dilemmas and negative consequences of the Methamphetamine use, coupled with the chemical affects on the brain. It is obviously nerve racking knowing that what you are doing is illegal and might have serious consequences if the user is discovered. There are also major negative consequences such as losing custody of your children, being fired from your job or even just being labeled a Meth user. Using often becomes a secret that is hidden at all costs, leading abusers to find new friends and disassociating with family members.

The chemical changes that occur in the brain often promote significant levels of anxiety and nervousness. The feeling of losing control is at the crux of this. If you ever have contact with a Meth user, you can easily see the chaos and mayhem that follow in their life. Everything seems so important and life changing regardless of how small the problem is. The stress level in a user is usually very high and interaction with them may even make you feel stressed out. I had a long conversation an addict that told me he hated using the drug because it made him paranoid and anxious and he said that he felt like someone was always watching him. (I could only respond with, "We were watching you", which added reality and humor to the conversation.)

Auditory and visual hallucinations are often the result of sleep deprivation and the ever present chemical imbalance produced by Meth. These hallucinations take many shapes and forms and can show themselves in almost any way imaginable. The thing to remember with these hallucinations is that they are very real to the user. Given that, the user will sound remarkably convincing in the stories they tell, with the hallucinations not being obvious to the person listening.

For example, I had someone call me to discuss a family member that they had concerns with. The general story was that this relative was seeing army men dressed in camouflage clothing conducting surveillance in his back yard. Now, first off I knew that there is always the possibility of a law enforcement agency conducting surveillance in any given neighborhood. I also know that a common hallucination in male Methamphetamine users is that they see "army men" dressed in camouflage clothing. The thing that raised concern with me was that the men were going through the trouble of getting dressed in camouflage but were also wearing bright orange stocking caps on their heads. That one part allowed me to pick up on the fact that this person might be experiencing Meth induced hallucinations.

Another area concerning these hallucinations is jealousy towards a user's spouse or partner. This is most common in male users. Many men that get high for any length of time will hear or see their spouse or girlfriend talking with another man. Needless to say, this is a great contributor to domestic disputes and the resulting violence. One woman said that her husband would look for fingerprints on the inside of their bedroom windows and tear holes in the walls of their house so he could see from room to room in an effort to catch her talking with the other man.

I have also heard stories of Meth contorting your worst fears into hallucinations. One user told me that he ran for miles in an attempt to get away from a snake that his dog told him was on him. As a result of this two way conversation with his dog, he swore the snake was on him, saw it on him and reacted like most of us would if there was a snake on us. The point that I am trying to make is that you should look and listen for things that seem convincing and maybe possible, but are more outlandish or almost sound like the plot from a best selling novel or movie.

Other common hallucinations are that of shadow people or demonic presences. Shadow people typically manifest after a person has been up for days at a time. They were best described by a user that told me that it was like catching a glimpse of someone passing by a window or down a hallway out of the corner of your eye. These shadow people are real enough for the user to look for them or to take a gun and randomly shoot into the woods.

Once I was on woodlands surveillance of a residence that was being used for Methamphetamine distribution. During this surveillance, I witnessed an abuser walk to the edge of the woods right where we were hiding and he started yelling at the top of his lungs saying that he saw someone. The scariest part was the fact that he was carrying a shotgun and started firing his shotgun into the trees just above our heads. Of course, I thought that he had seen us in the woods watching the house, but in all reality his violent and crazed behavior was caused by being strung out. (Like I said, my experiences with Meth are up close and personal.) The other common hallucination is that of demonic creatures often referred to by the user as the devil himself. This hallucination contributes to another Methamphetamine indicator which is the fascination with Satan or satanic material. We will talk more about this later in the book.

Paranoia, feelings of plotting against the user, and the user constantly talking of a conspiracy against them are common symptoms. Often the user will not trust anyone that is around them including their loved ones, old friends, new friends or even their drug source. They carry with them the belief that everyone is "out to get them." I have talked to many users that have explained that there is often no basis at all for this behavior and the conspiracy thoughts.

A young female told me that she sat in the back seat of a car and listened to two of her friends talk about the songs that were playing on the radio. She couldn't comprehend why talking about music was so important and assumed that they were talking in code about her and were plotting to "get her." Many users will feel that their own children or spouse is trying to get them arrested or get them into some type of trouble. This will cause the abuser to act out violently against the person that they think is conspiring against them. Often things like a misdialed telephone number, either incoming or outgoing, or an unusual piece of mail will send them into a rage about conspiracy.

Other users become "window watchers", a common term meaning that they will spend hours on end peering out a window waiting for something bad to happen. This usually ties back into the hallucinations, because eventually the brain begins to see the very thing that they are so paranoid about. Users that are afraid they will see the police will see imaginary patrol units drive by their house or that every car will be an undercover narcotics team surveying them. It might be an ex husband or wife that they think is spying on them or it might even be the federal government that has placed listening devices around their residence. On the mild side, the user may seem less paranoid and just appear to be unhappy and make comments about the government or the police or a family member always trying to ruin their life or a good time.

Often the symptoms become more serious and may mirror schizophrenic like behavior. Often doctors misdiagnose Meth addicts as schizophrenics and treat them as such because the symptoms are often exactly the same. Medicine that can be used to treat a schizophrenic patient can also curb the negative side effects of the drug's use. They will pursue doctors that will prescribe them schizophrenic medicines or they will illegally purchase and abuse medications like Xanax and valium because of their curbing effects. Marijuana may also be used for the similar reasons because of its calming traits.

Methamphetamine users will often lack focus, not only in their lives, but also in their everyday thoughts and conversations. A typical conversation with a user will often cover many different topics. At one moment they may talk about their finances and the next minute you are having a conversation about vacuuming the house. Often a Methamphetamine user might not be able to finish a sentence or train of thought. (This is often during immediate use.)

I can't help but think of the news article I read concerning two teens that died of exposure to cold weather in Nebraska during a snow storm early in 2005. Of course the reason they died medically was from exposure, but in reality their deaths were more attributed to their Meth use. These two young teens were unable to do the simple task of telling 911 operators where they were located in the midst of this storm, because they couldn't focus on describing their location. Once the rescuers arrived, they found that they more than 50 miles away from the teens' actual location. This is a sad, but often true, fact about Methamphetamine. Many users don't die from the drug use itself, but are injured or die from actions that they take under the influence.

Methamphetamine use, in my opinion, is very similar to a severe case of Attention Deficit Disorder where the users shows symptoms like an extreme need for attention, problems focusing on tasks, exaggerating or making up lies, as well as the inability to organize large projects or being prone to emotional outbursts. Of course, the major difference is that the Meth user's symptoms appear much worse than with mild to moderate Attention Deficit Disorder.

Methamphetamine use also has many other physical effects on the body that might be noted in a physical exam or by emergency medical personnel during some type unexpected contact with them. Profuse sweating is readily seen in avid users during inappropriate times, such as cold weather or at a resting activity level. Users often raise the core body temperature several degrees, experiencing a "Methamphetamine fever" of sorts. Often the user will be wringing with sweat and their hair and clothing will be soaked from perspiration. This may cause the user to not wear enough clothing in colder weather or may make them take their clothing off all together. The two kids from Nebraska that were mentioned earlier were not dressed appropriately for being out in a snow storm and the heaviest piece of clothing they had on was a sweatshirt.

The user will often have a rapid heart rate in excess of 180 beats per minute, causing the user to become catatonic or have exhibited unresponsiveness similar to a state of shock. The user's blood pressure, breathing and alertness will all be increased. A user's pupils become dilated. The user's tongue may swell and turn pale gray or white, occurring generally within 12 hours of use.

Most of the incidents that I have seen where these effects were present were in school-aged kids that had some type of physical reaction to the drug while they were in school. Often the child would become unresponsive and emergency medical personnel would be called to the scene. After a brief exam of the student all the above symptoms would be noted. Of course the student never admits to using

Meth so often the cause for the episode may go unexplained. The incidents where I have seen this happen most is when students increase their activity level during the day, most commonly during gym class.

Another common symptom for Methamphetamine users is the extended period of time that they go without sleep. Please understand that when I say without sleep, that I mean just that no sleep, no naps, no rest. Many users may go just a few days without sleep and other users will stay awake as much as 10 to 14 days. I spoke to a user once that told me that she had stayed up for three days straight after her very first use.

The increased energy is a desired effect that many "soccer moms" and single mother desire and is usually the effect that is seen most in those that snort the drug. Some users begin to keep up with schedules, kids and jobs. At first, they are able to accomplish more because their waking hours give them more time to accomplish more tasks. Meth actually makes their lives seem to be more organized and manageable during the first few weeks of use. Of course the deceptive side is that it brings the user back down to a place where the drug is needed just to keep up with the schedule, kids and job. This type of sleep deprivation alone would cause any non drug using person to experience paranoia and hallucinations.

Imagine yourself being awake with no rest for 24 hours or for two or three days at a time. Imagine what your mind and body would experience. Irritability and poor judgment are things that I know I experience when I am very tired and not well rested. Now imagine being up for 10 days without rest. Then add Methamphetamine to the equation and there is the making for a disaster.

Commonly, users will have to deal with issues of insomnia after they quit using the drug and these effects may last for weeks or months after the drug has not been used. These symptoms are difficult to deal with and may fuel the user to relapse. Anyone with insomnia can tell you the misery that they deal with on a daily basis. The problem that often arises from these extended times without sleep is that the users find themselves crashing or passing out when their bodies can no longer stay conscious. The biggest danger of this crash doesn't get the attention it deserves. That danger is not directed toward the user, but at those that are around him or when the crash happens.

A young woman that I went to church with for years found herself addicted to Methamphetamine and her use ended with a literal crash. She had been using for two years, and was at a time when she had been up for days with no rest. Her body couldn't take any more, and she passed out behind the wheel of her car and crossed the center line striking another car head on. She severely injured herself and the driver of the other vehicle. These types of accidents are common when users get behind the wheel after many days of no sleep. Another story that I heard about in the field was about a women that had been up for days on end when she decided to take a bath with her baby. The young mother crashed and woke to find her child drowned in the tub next to her Meth taking another innocent bystander.

The opposite of the sleep loss is also true and many users will experience episodes of long, catatonic like sleep. Many parents see this more than they do the sleeplessness because their child will show up on the front door after weeks of use and use their home as a place to rest and recover from a binge. Many users will not even get up to eat or use the restroom during these rests that last two to three days. The reason that these users don't need to get up to use the restroom is because there body literally has no liquid or food waste to get rid of. (We will cover the reason for these indicators later in the book.)

Users are nearly impossible to wake up when they are in this state. On numerous search warrants I have been on, I encountered addicts that I couldn't shake awake. On one particular case, my unit and I were conducting an arrest on two Methamphetamine users that had sold one ounce to an undercover police officer. The male suspect was arrested. During the arrest we noticed the female suspect sleeping in the front passenger seat of the vehicle that they had arrived in. As we approached the car, I noticed that she was sitting on a handgun. I knew that if we woke her before she was taken into custody she might use the gun against us. I tried the door and it was locked. I took a safe position and tried to beat on the window to wake her. We kept trying until the window shattered and we were able to drag her out away from the handgun and into custody. She did not wake up until she was on the ground and being placed into handcuffs.

Decreased appetite is often an indicator, resulting in dramatic weight loss. I have been told by doctors that the normally occurring chemical in our body that suppresses hunger is overproduced during Meth use, causing a major loss of appetite. Now I don't completely understand all the medical reasons why the appetite is suppressed, but I do know that one of the most damaging effects of the drug, and one of the most easily seen signs, is the emaciating effects on users.

There is no exact formula for the weight loss, but it is not uncommon to see a user lose about 10 pounds a month with regular use. This indicator is most often seen in female users and many of them will lose so much that they only weigh 85 or 90 pounds. Because weight loss is one of the more commonly known Methamphetamine user indicators, many people refuse to believe that their loved one is using because the person that they are worried about is not losing any weight. Please understand that in some cases, a Methamphetamine user will not lose their appetite or weight during use.

I recall one user in particular that told me that she never lost any weight during use and would often become hungry or eat more regular after she smoked. I was involved with a number of her arrests and I can look back at her booking pictures and say that she was right. There was no notable weight loss over several years of use. Now those type people are few and far between.

Part of the idea behind this book came from this effect that I had seen in so many users. Just as I got ready to start writing, I had taken a trip to Andersonville, Georgia which is the site of a National Prisoner of War Museum and the site of a huge prisoner of war stockade during the American Civil War. Prisoners in Andersonville were subjected to many cruel and extreme situations, one of which was being starved to death. As I looked at the pictures of these living skeletons, I realized how much these prisoners reminded me of so many Meth addicts that I knew. I also quickly realized that these users were also trapped inside a stockade of their own addiction. Even more unusual was the fact that the starvation and imprisonment of the user is a self imposed sentence. And so, Prisoners of Meth was born.

Dehydration from decreased fluid intake is one of the more unusual but common side effects of Methamphetamine use. Fluid intake is minimized or halted all together because the body has the tendency to retain urine, resulting in an intense burning sensation while urinating. Many users will purposefully not drink fluids because of this. The result is significant dehydration, commonly seen on the hands and lips, both turning chapped and pale. During an interview I had with a Methamphetamine user he admitted that he often did not drink any fluids until he felt his kidneys aching. I researched the internet for more information and located one report where a woman who was an avid user, had her bladder rupture because of the amount of urine she retained.

Many Methamphetamine users will prefer dark rooms and avoid sunlight or bright lights. As I mentioned earlier, an addict's eyes become dilated and light sensitive during use. Considering also that you are up both night and day, choosing to operate at night is not as unusual as it would be for us. A user that is very close to me personally once said, "Your nights become days and your days become your nights."

Another one of the well known outwardly visible signs of Methamphetamine use is the sores that develop all over the body. These sores resemble chicken pox and scabby scars. Some may be small while others may look more like large infected sores. Methamphetamine users refer to these sores as Meth Mites, Crank Bugs or Speed Bumps.

In my experience there are a few reasons why these sores develop. The first reason is a result of a compulsive need to pick at the skin or pick at sores that are caused by external reasons, like bug bites or any other way that we occasionally injure ourselves. A user will pick at these places, making them worse through the aggravation. The user might also feel "crawling" just under the skin and try to scratch these "bugs" out from underneath their skin, resulting in breaks in the skin that turn into sores. One user I knew actually took a razor blade and cut out what he thought was a spider under his skin from the back of his calf.

Another reason for the sores is because approximately 30 to 50 percent of Methamphetamine that is ingested into the body is not used and passed out of the body through either urine or the skin. When Meth passes through the skin, it can cause infected pores which are picked at and then turn to the sores. Often these sores will develop a more random pattern on the face, neck, chest and legs and more closely resemble bad acne or chicken pox.

I spoke to an addict during an intervention that showed me two scars on her face; one on her cheek and another between her eyebrows that she said where from Crank Bugs. She stated that as her use increased, she began developing hard knots under her skin that felt like a pimple but would not come to the surface of her skin. Of course her habit caused her to pick out of her control. She told me that eventually she was able to push what she described as a chunk of salt-like crystal out of the sore. This was enough to make my skin crawl, something that doesn't happen often. A user might also "trap door" with these sores, which means that the sores that develop will be picked away from the skin just enough to introduce a needle into the body for injecting Methamphetamine and then the scab is placed back over the wound to cover up the injection site. Many of the users that I talk to tell me the usual lies that are made up to cover for these sores. Acne, hives, and sun poisoning are all excuses that I have heard over and over again for the sores.

The greatest concern about Methamphetamine passing through the skin and urine doesn't stop with Crank Bugs and trap doors. An even more graphic example of how serious the addiction of Methamphetamine can be is called "recycling". Let me explain.

You see if we as non-users know that Meth passes through the urine then users also know this. For years, I have seen and heard about addicts keeping their urine in jars and milk jugs. For the longest time I could not understand why they'd do this. I finally got the nerve and asked one of them to explain. He told me that because there is so much Meth that is passed in the urine, an addict will "recycle it". This meant that the user will keep their own and other persons urine, and then cook the urine down to recover the Methamphetamine that is contained in it. The addict will reuse or sell this "recycled" Meth a second time, a third time, and on and on.

Another common indicator of Methamphetamine use is an overall rough or careless appearance in the user. This is easily seen in clothing, personal hygiene and in the user's hands, nails and teeth. Most users lose interest in washing or changing clothes from day to day. The user will also develop what my partners and I call "crank hands". This is a combination of dirt and filth on the hands as well as the dehydration that we have already discussed along with bad cuticles and nails. Often a user will pick at their hands and fingers resulting in poor skin condition of the hands and fingers.

A Methamphetamine user's teeth will also show intense and serious wear. A user's teeth might look rotted or show patchy discoloration or completely fall out starting with the teeth in the front. Many young users will loose their teeth, which results in a poor self image and promotes further use. I talked with several local dentists in my area and I have read stories from others describing how Meth has changed their jobs. So many young and attractive kids are going for major dental work, including pulling rotten teeth and having to get partials or dentures.

Many Methamphetamine users will develop obsessive compulsive disorders (OCDs) as a result of their use. One of the most unusual examples of this I heard while I was interviewing a young man that had been convicted of murdering his father in a drug-induced rage. Of course my interest in talking with him was about the murder and how Meth contributed to the crime, but one of the interesting things that I learned was about one of his OCDs. Apparently this young man was raised in church and the Christian religion was a very important part of his life. As a result of his faith he had been taught at length about God's Trinity the Father, the Son and the Holy Ghost. As his Methamphetamine use became advanced he developed a fascination with any item that came in increments of three or any task that was preformed in threes.

We commonly see "tweaking" and "pack ratting. Tweaking is a common

Methamphetamine induced OCD. Many times a user will begin to take anything electronic apart like televisions, video cassette recorders or any small electronic device in search of listening devices that we commonly call "bugs." Because of this rampant paranoia, they'll tear everything up in their house looking for said devices. Of course taking these items apart is a lot easier than putting them back together. So, the result is a room full of things that are broken apart and lying around in pieces.

The second common OCD is "pack-ratting." Many users will begin to collect things for no apparent rhyme or reason. This may be a result of taking things in on trade in exchange for drugs and is often an indicator for selling Meth. Another reason for the pack ratting, and probably the primary reason, is the overall paranoia that causes the users to want to keep things with an "all mine" kind of attitude. I have seen all types of things kept by a user from empty disposable lighters to worthless electronic equipment.

Of course Methamphetamine shows itself in many other obsessive type behaviors that range from picking out all your eyebrows, obsessive cleaning or writing and doodling in excessive amounts. For some reason Meth grabs hold of a little quirk that you have, and brings it to the forefront of your life and then amplifies it to make it an obsession. Anytime that a loved one begins showing signs of an OCD it is cause for concern and should be addressed.

Another indicator is sex itself. It is hard to explain, but Methamphetamine and sex go hand in hand. Sex and the drug are probably so closely related because of the overproduction of dopamine and the destruction of the same that occur in the brain. The layers of sex and Methamphetamine are several folds.

Methamphetamine use in and of itself can cause an increased desire for sex. Many users that I have talked with would tell you that sex is better while using Methamphetamine. What they usually mean is that the sex is usually lengthier, more often and more explicit while they are using. The problem is that more often and more explicit usually means more dangerous and harmful. Methamphetamine acts as an anesthetic of sorts and allows the users to perform sexually for longer periods of time without climax.

Often a male Methamphetamine user will have trouble performing as his drug use increases and this may be an area of embarrassment which turns to anger and violence against his partner. As the Methamphetamine use continues, and dopamine becomes harder and harder to trigger, a user has to either use a prescription medication for erectile dysfunction to assist in performance, or often the user will delve into areas of sexual behavior that is not normal for them in order to trigger a release of dopamine. This behavior will often result in various problems.

Infidelity in marriage is often a result of this explicit sexual behavior because one of the partners does not want to participate in the unusual sexual acts and the user will have to go out and find another willing partner to engage in this activity. Many long term and healthy marriages end in divorce because of this, and I have talked to many users that refer to their husband or wife as an "ex" because of the infidelity that occurred during their use. Users will often introduce sex toys into their activity to assist them in being able to perform.

In the law enforcement community, traffic stops result in the arrest of more drivers possessing Methamphetamine and also the discovery of large amounts of sexually explicit materials found in the vehicle. For example, bondage and pornographic materials are often used by Methamphetamine users away from the privacy of their home. In the law enforcement community, we often comment about being able to tell how far someone is in their use by the size of their pornography collection. There is very rarely an instance while we are serving search warrants for Meth that homemade or commercially bought pornography is not present at a user's home, usually in large volume.

The greatest area of concern is when this unusual sexual behavior spills over into innocent children's lives. A user that told me that when he used Meth, he would have to go to daycare centers and watch children while masturbating because that was the only way that he could find sexual satisfaction. Many children are the target of their parents or care takers sexual energy. This is often the point where many users are turned into law enforcement agencies or family and children services because of the abuse against the children. I have worked several investigations where a mother will have sex with her young son's friends and will often give them Meth in order to keep them coming back for more of the drug and sex.

Lastly, Methamphetamine users will leave behind evidence in the form of drug related paraphernalia. Note that the list ranges from user to user and from day to day. Using by way of needle injection or "banging" is on the rise. Throughout my career I have seen a few heroin addicts and a few other drugs used by injection as well, but it was just not that common in the outlying metro Atlanta area. When ICE use increased, the amount of needles we began to find on traffic stops and search warrants increased as well. I have talked with many younger users that have shared needles, not having grown up with the AIDS scare like many others of us did.

Propane style torches and lighters are also typically used by Meth smokers. ICE will not burn until it reaches at least 180 degrees, so a high heat flame is needed for its use. A regular flame lighter won't burn Methamphetamine like it will crack cocaine. Often these "blue" flame lighters or "wind proof" lighters are kept near the cash register in local convenience stores and are purchased by users in the dozens.

As the user increases the amount of Methamphetamine that they smoke, both in amount and frequency, a larger torch is needed. Many times the user will turn to commercial type torches like ones that are used in plumbing work. These torches are readily available in any hardware or large retail store. They allow the user to keep the flame lit longer and make it easier to take in greater amounts of the drug. These torches come in many shapes and sizes but the most common torch size is about the size of a coffee thermos and has a brass nozzle that attaches to the top of it. These nozzles are reusable and Methamphetamine users will keep these nozzles close by like in their pants pockets or laying around in their bedroom.

Also look for small jeweler's bags or the corners of plastic sandwich bags. These small baggies, which look like tiny Ziploc sandwich bags, were often called "crack baggies" in the 80s and 90s, but were renamed "sacks" as their use in packaging Meth increased. These bags are sold legally because they have other uses like packaging small jewels, stamps or coins. Of course, most respectable diamond dealers don't prefer to transport their gems or rare coins in plastic bags with cartoon characters or the silhouettes of naked woman on them. Another common packaging for "user" amounts of Methamphetamine is the corner of plastic bags that have been cut in a triangular shape, the Methamphetamine placed inside and tied off to look like small knotted pouches.

Glass pipes are yet another indicator. These pipes can be purchased at convenience stores and are sold legally in most states. These pipes are generally six inch hollow glass tubes with a round glass ball on one end. When they are sold in the stores, they are sold as trinkets and will have a silk rose inside them and usually have a sticker on the outside that say, "I love you" or "Happy Valentines Day." After being purchased, a Methamphetamine user will place a small amount of the drug inside the glass bowl portion, burn it until it smokes and then ingest the smoke as it emits from the pipe.

After a pipe is used to smoke Meth, it appears black or burned on the bowl end and may have a white residue progressing up the glass stem. Standard round light bulbs are used in a similar fashion. A light bulb is used by making a hole in the metal end or by removing the ceramic nipple from the end which releases the ceramic end and the filament, which is removed. All that is left is a glass bowl.

Aluminum foil is also commonly used. A small square of it is taken from the roll and the Meth is placed right directly on the foil, heated and inhaled. The little foil pieces are often left behind and will have one side that is burnt or blackened. I have talked to many parents that have found these pieces lying in garbage cans or in bathroom waste baskets. Although foil is such a common household item, this is probably one of the greatest indicators for illegal drug use and should not be ignored.

Many users will develop a preoccupation with violence and death as well as a fascination with satanic material. My first experience with this was in a mobile home park where I was assisting with serving a search warrant. I remember walking in the side door of the trailer and started my search as I had done many times before. As I began to search looking around the living room, I noticed a leather jacket pinned to the wall with the back of the jacket facing out. On this leather jacket there was a beautiful portrait of Jesus painted on it. Located around the jacket, like the numbers on a clock, were several packaged children's toys which were small action figures.

Now these action figures were not toys that are for children, but are geared more towards adults and were from well known horror movies. These figures were grotesque and what many would consider evil. I could not get the suspect to tell me why he had arranged the jacket and the action figures in this manner, but I had read before that this could have been an attempt to contain good in the trailer home. Several months later I found something similar on the basement wall of another user's house. This was the same design with a cross in the middle and approximately 12 symbols that I didn't recognize placed around the cross like the numbers on a clock. I've also seen a large wooden cross altered with horns protruding from it.

One of the strangest things that I've ever seen came about when I was serving a search warrant at a Meth user's home. This house was decorated from top to bottom with every type of murderous and evil prop that you could imagine. In the kitchen there was a full statue of the devil, complete with wings, sitting at the kitchen table. In front of this statue was a decorative plate that had engravings of skulls and bones on it. In the plate were lifelike rubber ears and fingers complete with blood as if they had just been cut off. Along a shelf in the kitchen that stretched from one end to the other were what I would call Halloween masks of the goriest kind; severed heads and monster masks that looked real and even spooked me. There was also a life size and realistic full human skeleton hanging from a noose attached to the ceiling.

I could go on and on about every room being decorated in the same manner. The den had life like severed arms and legs along with a digital clock that said "Satan loves you" in a digital read out that popped up every few seconds. The suspect's bedroom had pictures of the devil and even more life-like busts of severed and mutilated heads. The most eerie part of it all was when we noticed the black lights all over the house.

After turning out the regular lights and turning on the black lights, the house lit up with what looked like one big crime scene. There were outlines of bodies on the wall and writings that were written to seem as if they were in blood that said things like "we are all doomed" and other references to death and hell. As the search of the residence continued, it was apparent that this man would invite his friends over, get high and seemingly embrace the hallucinations of Satan and demons that they were having.

It seems that the obvious signs of this fascination are seen most easily in those users that embrace their fears and hallucinations and even begin to enjoy them as visits from the devil. Also, many users will surround themselves with gory and violent movies and images. A user may begin to experience feelings of suicide, and often, contemplating suicide is a scary alternative to dealing with a Methamphetamine addiction. As scary is the fact that many users don't follow through with killing themselves because then they know that they won't be able to get their hands on any Meth.

Many abusers will develop a fascination with arming themselves with knives or guns, which may progress into other destructive things like pipe bombs or other explosives. Users that already have an inclination to possess firearms may carry two or three at a time. Others with no prior interest may purchase a firearm. The danger is that many users also increase their willingness to use firearms during their use and may commits acts of violence that they never would if they weren't using Methamphetamine to begin with.

The installation or fascination with closed circuit television cameras and monitors may also become apparent with prolonged use. Often the paranoia makes the users want to see outside their walls and peer into the darkness. They want to know who is visiting their house before the visitors arrive or hide from certain people (including the police). They will install these cameras to see down the driveway or out the front door. These cameras might be hidden in birdhouses or actually hidden in the walls of the home. These systems might be hardwired into the home or a user may be happy with a less expensive, wireless version that can be moved from place to place.

Many people ask me about the smell that Methamphetamine leaves behind after it has been smoked. That is probably one of the hardest things to explain. After burning, Meth leaves a waxy and greasy smell on the clothing of a user and on the fabric upholstery in their furniture, vehicle, etc. Imagine if the times that you left a restaurant where the cooks were using a griddle and heavy grease. The strong greasy smell that is left on your clothing is the closest thing that I can think of as to what Methamphetamine smells like.

In the end, it is easy to see the wake of evidence that is left behind in a Methamphetamine user's life. Recognizing the problem, although it appears hard, may be the easiest part of this problem. The next chapters will cover the ABC's of how to begin to deal with the problem that you have that is a result of someone else's addiction. Let's get started on dealing with this problem.

The ABC's of Methamphetamine Intervention

A   *Acknowledge that there might be a problem.*

The thought that someone you love is abusing Methamphetamine seems to be so hard for many people to fully grasp. Like I said earlier, I have taken many calls from parents that have found a Methamphetamine pipe or pieces of burnt aluminum foil in their child's bedroom and refused to believe that there child was using, much less may be addicted to it. Something in our minds wants to expect the best and refuse to accept the worst.

You might be thinking that it is easy for me to say from where I'm sitting, but I have been where you are. And to be honest, I failed the test. I didn't know the indicators or what to look for. I did, however, have a gut feeling that there was something wrong. I chose to write it off as a phase that the person was going through. You see, I had someone very close to me not only using Meth, but addicted to it. I can look back now and see some of the signs that I know to look for now. But at that time, I had no idea there was a problem.

I guess I thought there was no way my loved one had a problem because there was no way that they would use drugs in the beginning. I did not even want to acknowledge that there was a possibility of a problem. I wish I had this book and the knowledge that I have now, back then. You do have this book though and if you are seeing the indicators and signs that there is a problem then acknowledge that there is a problem and begin to move forward. Write down your thoughts and the indicators that you see so that you can have them to address later.

B   *Begin to accept that there is a problem.*

Acknowledging that there might be a problem is much different than accepting the problem. Accepting that there is a problem sets us in motion, while acknowledging that there might be a problem only causes us to wonder and makes us sit around wondering. Understand that you will probably have thoughts and questions about what part you played in your loved one's deciding to use Methamphetamine. Parents wonder how they failed their child and husbands and wives wonder how they fail short in their relationship. This might be called the "Why?" stage as well.

I guess accepting the problem goes hand in hand with wanting to know why. The fact of the matter is that there are a thousand reasons why people use Meth. Accepting that they did use it often results in having to begin to accept why they used. Of course dealing with the reasons that someone started using drugs is just as important as the fact that they used Methamphetamine at all. Write down any thoughts that you have or any issues that you may want to discuss with your loved one when the time comes about why you think they might have even used Methamphetamine in the first place.

C   *Choose to do something about the problem.*

As I just mentioned, acceptance of the problem often compels us into some type of action and it is a good decision to choose to do something about the problem. I have seen many people, especially parents, who choose to stay out of their child's affairs and remain passive as they watch the problem unfold. I guess my question to those people is, "If not you, then who?" Who do you think will do something to help? Remember that your loved one has surrounded themselves with other Methamphetamine users and the last thing that those people want is to have someone around them to get clean.

I have found that Meth makes nightmares and clichés -especially "misery loves company"- become a reality. Their Methamphetamine friends won't help them. You have to choose to get involved. Their use is not a fad or a stage. Your involvement might make the difference in life and death.

I have had many parents tell me that they don't want to get involved in their child's affairs. I tell them if they don't want to get involved, then they should get their child's final affairs in order. Ignoring the problem is just like closing the door on their coffin. That is true for any loved one that is using. It is probably just as hard for friends to meddle in another friend's business, especially with something as serious as a drug addiction.

D   *Develop a plan of action.*

Begin to write down a plan of action using E though Z. Make sure that this plan is based on what facts you know and not based on the emotions that you have. Many plans go awry because of anger or pity. As an example, many parents bail their children out of jail after a Meth related arrest, even though they have been told not to. That decision is based on the love and compassion that we have for our loved ones and not on what might be best for the abuser.

It is hard to take an objective point of view, and it is even harder to trust people that you have just met like the treatment providers and police officers that advise you to leave them in jail. Try and begin to listen to those who do have an objective point of view. There is nothing like having to make the comment, "I should have listened to you to begin with." So, take as logical approach as you can muster and begin to think about how you want to help.

Use the note taking pages at the end of this book to keep up with all that you do in the midst of this tornado that you are walking into. I have seen many parents with pockets full of scratch pads, napkins and matchbooks with notes written on them. Keeping things straight in your mind makes your thoughts easier to relay to the right person at the right time.

E   *Enlist help wherever you can from people that will be able to assist you in developing your plan.*

There is plenty of help that is available, but finding it is often very difficult. Let me give you a few places where you might find help. Your church is often a great place to begin looking.

Church is often a place to find resources including recovering users that have found a way to stop using and they might be able to share with you their successes. There are many treatment plans and support groups that are located at local churches, as well as written resources including the Bible as means of assisting in empowering you to develop a plan. The good thing about a local church, is that their resources are often free an important consideration as you undertake this.

Secondly, friends of your loved one may be a great resource for information and help. Although many the user's friends are going to run away scared if you try to talk to them about Methamphetamine use there are a few out there that are clean and want to be part of the solution. Chances are, they are looking for a way to help the same as you are. Some of the best friendships are developed as a result of a Meth addiction. These friends can provide you with another point of view at looking at the problem.

Treatment providers and drug counselors are of course tremendous resources of help and information. Their knowledge can be fundamental in formulating a plan because they work in the field every day and have different models in place that they may be able to plug you into. We will talk more about treatment providers and treatment options under letter H. I will also give you tips on how to choose the plan right for your circumstances.

Although it might not be comfortable, employing the help of your local police or sheriff's office, or a state or federal law enforcement agency is a good option. When you initially contact a law enforcement agency, you can ask to remain anonymous as to your loved one's identity while you are asking for their help. Be up front and tell them that you are trying to get someone some help for a Methamphetamine problem and that you want to talk to someone about your circumstances.

Make sure to write down names and phone numbers, as well as the times that you talked to the officer or agent so that you can remember who and when you talked with whom. If needed, you can call that specific person back. Most agencies are large and this will save you from having to repeat your story. Explain to them why you think that there is a problem based on the indicators that you have noticed and let them form an opinion based on what you tell them. Having someone agree with you that there is a problem may be the encouragement that you need to keep moving forward.

Be willing to develop a relationship with the officer you contact, and be willing to share with them any information that you gain dealing with your loved one's problem. In law enforcement, it is often a game of give and take. You can develop a good relationship based on providing information on local drug houses and drug dealers that you root out as you become more involved. I will be the first to admit that you may have a bad experience with contacting a law enforcement agent, but if you are patient and honest I think that you might see that they would be willing to help. On the other hand, don't be afraid to call another agency or another officer if you aren't getting the attention that you want.

A family doctor or mental health specialist might be a good resource to contact and have on standby for when he or she is needed. They can provide the medical treatment that is necessary when dealing with the needs of a recovering addict. Not all doctors are up to date or are well- versed on the problems surrounding Meth use, but there are those like Dr. Boddy that become specialists of sorts in treating Methamphetamine related problems. As you have learned about drug use, there may be the need for the treatment of the symptoms and a good doctor that you trust is a valuable asset from this point in your plan.

Other family members or friends that you know are clean are usually a good group of people to get involved and can become a working support group. No one wants to see an old friend or family member destroy themselves. The more people that you are able to surround yourself and the user with, the better and easier things might be when you confront them about their problem. Everyone has a favorite family member or old buddy that they have special feelings for and it could work in your favor having them around when a problem arises or when an emotional wall is put up that you can't overcome.

F   *Find out what has worked for others concerning their problems with Methamphetamine.*

Get on the internet, talk to other people, research and find out what plans worked better for others and then mold it to suit your needs. I have found that the internet is a great way to begin finding out what exactly you are going to do. Just take a moment to sit in front of a computer, either at home or at the public library and type the word "Methamphetamine" into any search engine. There will be no lack for the number of pages that will come back about the topic. Research and read what you can about the topic and then as your knowledge of the drug increases you will be able to ask the search engine to look for more specific topics like "Methamphetamine treatment options" or "Methamphetamine prison sentences."

Concentrating on success stories is probably a better option at this point. Try not to focus on the horror stories that you find. Thinking and reading positively will help you keep focused and encouraged. Let me tell you that the problem that surrounds Methamphetamine and our community is complex, dark and often overwhelming. Let's not pretend, the odds are going to be against you, so looking at negative stories is going to frustrate you.

On the other hand, there are many great success stories about recovering Methamphetamine addicts and these type stories are great motivators and sources of information. Knowledge is power. Read as much as you can about Meth. The internet can also lead to groups of people that are familiar with the problem and different type support groups.

"Mother against Methamphetamine Abuse" and "Crystal Meth Anonymous" are two nationwide groups that have plenty of people willing to just talk with you about what you are going through. Many of the people you may have contact with could possibly be recovering addicts themselves and can give you pointers on what helped them or what they think would have helped them. Be aware though that as with any other problem, people involved in combating Methamphetamine are very passionate and will sometimes be forceful in helping you with your problem. It is just that people involved in the problem, including myself, want so much to help someone get away from this evil. Tell them right up front that you are collecting information and that you will consider everything that they are saying. Developing a plan of attack based on what one person did that worked for them may not work for you.

G *Get all the information that you can that is specific to your situation.*

This is a tricky situation that has many "gray" areas, but you can become your own investigator. Let me say that at no time do I condone taking the law into your own hands. I don't condone toting firearms around in search of your children, and I definitely do not recommend that you find yourself committing a criminal act in the pursuit to save your loved one.

I have seen examples of each of these mistakes and usually it is with the parents of a user. A passionate dad that learns that his baby girl is on Methamphetamine is often the one who wants to go to the local drug dealer's house and physically hurt the person that is giving the drug to their child. Take this energy, anger and all the emotion that you may be experiencing and turn it into something constructive.

The easiest thing that you can do is be able to think back about all you have seen, as well as begin to open your eyes to what is revolving around their use. Write down all you can remember and all you are seeing without getting physically involved with the situation. Write down the names, address, vehicle descriptions and license plate numbers, cell phone numbers and any other information that you think is pertinent. Ask questions, ask questions and then ask some more questions of anyone willing to talk with you. Write down their name and number unless you agree to keep them confidential and do all you can to keep your word and not pass along to anyone where the information they gave you came from. Ask them directly if your loved one is using Methamphetamine, ask them how long they have been using, where they are getting it from, where they hide it, when they use it, how they use it and where they use it. Not only is this great information to give to the police so that you can help put the supplier in jail, but also it prepares you to get all the needed information to develop an appropriate plan.

Believe it or not, it does matter how long and in which way your loved one is using Methamphetamine. People that smoke or inject Methamphetamine have a much harder time with recovery than someone that has only snorted or eaten the drug. Also, injecting the drug would usually indicate a longer addiction as snorting might indicate a shorter time of use. Find out where your loved one usually is when using and who the people might be that they are likely to be with when they are using. All this information can be used in many ways including when we get to the letter "R." I will say it again write down everything you learn in my companion workbook so that you can keep this information close at hand and in order.

I really can't give you a list of everything that a law enforcement officer might want or need to initiate an investigation, but I know that first and last names, addresses and tag numbers of possible dealers are always good things to forward. Understand though that what appears to be a great piece of intelligence to you may not be that important to the police in being able to investigate someone. Cell phone numbers and phone records are good intelligence, but are not very helpful in an immediate needs investigation.

Now, like I said, I do not condone physically getting involved in your own investigation. But I have seen, and do not stand in the way of a parent that says they are going to get their young children from out of the situation they are in and bring them home. Some of the most inspirational stories are the ones from parents that went on a vigil to find, follow and harass their children into coming home.

There is nothing like seeing a 110 pound mom stand up in the face of a huge drug dealer and tell them that they are going to do all that is in their power to see them behind bars. Again, this is not the smartest and safest thing that a parent can do. To the parents of an addicted child, as a police officer, I say do everything within the law to get the help that your child needs. As a parent, I say do whatever needs to be done to help you child. Allow your conscience, good morals and smart decisions guide you.

H *Have several treatment options ready to go.*

Fortunately, there are a number of options available. I am very familiar with the treatment area of Methamphetamine addiction, and although I am not a certified counselor or licensed provider, I do have experience in what programs I have seen have good success. I also have had my fair share of "unofficial" interventions with many Methamphetamine addicts.

I can say for sure that the one thing I do know about treatment is that a person that does not want treatment or someone that thinks they do not need treatment is virtually untreatable. This also plays an important part in the letter "R" that I have been building up to, so I'll say again that someone that does not want treatment generally cannot be treated. When someone gets to the point that they desire treatment, it is imperative to have something ready to go because that window of opportunity doesn't stay open very long.

There are typically two types of treatment options available — "in facility" programs and the "outpatient" or "support group" type treatment settings. I generally recommend an in facility treatment plan for Meth addicts. As a general rule, I say that the time of treatment needed should mirror the time that they used from six months up to 18 months. That means that if someone has been using six months then don't be fooled into believing that a 90 day program will work. Sometimes when someone is very eager to get help the time that they need in treatment can be reduced, but as a rule, many users need several months just to get the Methamphetamine out of their systems.

I spoke to one successful recovering addict that started a local Crystal Methamphetamine Anonymous support group in our area. He agreed that support group and outpatient settings are generally what a Methamphetamine user needs after they have completed an in-house program. We agreed that just going straight into a support group type setting will not limit the user's access to the drug and a risk for relapse increases with that kind of freedom. He told me that in his personal experience with addiction and recovery, it took nearly 10 months before he could clear his mind enough to even concentrate on getting better. I think that because Meth affects the memory centers of the brain it is hard for addicts to get to a point to where they can concentrate on the idea of getting better.

Often, in-house treatment facilities are located miles or even states away from the user's home. This separation causes the inability for users to easily leave and get their hands on the drug. Many addicts also admit that Methamphetamine is a 24 hour a day problem and there has to be a full day of structured environment that offers support in some way or another for the problem. A few hours a day or a few hours a week, just doesn't help them fight off the desire to continue use. So, how do you decide on an in-house treatment facility that is right for your loved one? That is a good question.

The internet, past users and local recommendations are all ways to find the right place for your situation. Remember that you are not looking for a treatment center for you, but one for your loved one so take that into consideration. You should find a place that has a history of successful treatment. Not always, but a place that has been in business a longer time has greater reliability.

In the tidal wave of Methamphetamine addiction, many different treatment facilities are popping up with cure-all methods for solving the problem of Methamphetamine addiction. Make sure that the personnel at the treatment facility have some type of recognized license or degree in the area of mental health or drug treatment. Make sure that your provider choice specializes in Methamphetamine treatment. Many drug treatment providers are not willing to admit that their short term program is inefficient in dealing with this type of addiction. Make them explain to you the treatment plan, make sure that it sounds sensible and ask why they believe that the plan only needs to be short term.

Find out what the expenses are for the treatment plan because this may be an immediate deciding factor as to whether your loved one can attend or not. If you cannot afford the treatment, then you cannot afford the treatment, and considering them is not an option. Move on to some other plan that you can afford.

Often insurance plans will not pay for treatment involving Methamphetamine addiction. If you are lucky, you might have insurance to pay for the treatment and this might open other avenues. Treatment can range from free to as much as thousands of dollars a week, so plan accordingly and talk with your insurance provider early on. Make sure to jot down who, when and what was said in the conversations with your provider.

I will admit that I am partial to faith-based treatment plans and they seem to have a high rate of success. I believe the primary reason for this is that the people that attend often want the treatment and are therefore more treatable. Contacting your local church may be a way to plug into one of these programs and often they are minimal in expense because they are supported by the church. These programs also teach changing life skills, in addition to dealing with the addiction. The bottom line is that there are good programs out there. Just do your research.

You may choose, or your loved one might choose, the other option of outpatient or support group treatment. This might be for someone that is a new user or for someone that has previously completed some type in-house treatment plan. These support groups are fantastic for someone that is on the road to recovery, but needs the support of their group to stay strong. The problem is that there are often few places like this available to the community particularly if you live in a rural community. Because of this, finding something close to you may be very difficult and an out of state, in house treatment facility may be your best option.

I can tell you that if someone close to me tried Methamphetamine just once, I would at the minimum have them in some type support group treatment plan or drug counseling. I have talked to many recovered addicts that have been clean for years and still attend regular meetings of their chosen support group, some on a daily basis.

The important thing is that you have more than one suitable option ready because the first one might not be the one that your loved one locks into. I would also suggest that you travel to and visit any facility that you plan to offer as an option. This is not an uncommon practice, and if you are going to bet your loved one's life on the treatment plan, you should be very sure about it. Just remember that treatment is the only true option for quitting. I personally know users that have quit on their own without any type of treatment, but this is a rarity that is seldom realized.

I   *Initiate your plan into action.*

At some point all your planning must be placed into action. Whether your loved one is at a point of desperation, sitting in a jail or have no idea that you know there is a problem confronting them is something that you must do. You may choose a professional intervention specialist to assist you in this and often this works well in a surprise situation. You may choose a family intervention, or you may use subtle hints to ease into the problem.

Regardless of the method you choose, use all that you have learned to begin to address the problem. I recommend that you begin any intervention by reassuring the person that you love them unconditionally. At this point, you begin addressing the problems and symptoms that you have seen and begin to give reasons or ultimatums for them to quit using.

J   _Just expect the worst in their reaction and yours._

The first thing that you can expect from anyone you are confronting about their Meth use is lies. To be blunt, there is something about Methamphetamine that makes everything a user says come out as half truths or no truth at all. Of course no one wants to be honest about the fact that they have a problem, and if they are denying it to themselves they are definitely not going to admit it to you.

One common mistake many people make when confronting an abuser is the intervener believes that the user will crumble under the pressure and admit to their use when they are confronted. To someone not using Methamphetamine, it is easy to see the signs of use and we think that they can't help but admit that there are signs as well. The truth is that the user does see the signs and symptoms of their use and they are usually prepared to make excuses for the symptoms if they are ever confronted about them or if there are ever any questions asked about their use.

So, what happens is that the loved one confronts the user and the user is able to fire back with responses, which are somewhat believable, as to the reasons for their symptoms. Before the conversation is over, the loved one has begun to doubt themselves, and even might doubt that the person they are confronting is using. I have heard all types of reasons that are given for Meth symptoms like the sores being attributed to the hives or mosquito bites. Of course things like stress, sickness or panic attacks are common reasons given for the weight loss. I have even heard users give the excuse that they are taking cold medicine or inhaled fumes from a fish aquarium that caused a positive result on a Methamphetamine urinalysis test.

Stress, work related issues, or "just needing to get away" might be reasons given for them being absent from their family life. Now there might be the possibility that one excuse is true for one of the symptoms, but rest assured that there is little chance someone who is showing four or five of the Meth use symptoms is not using the drug. Don't feel like you have to convince them what the signs are because they won't admit to you that they see them.

You can also expect anger or a guilt trip in response to your questioning. The user may lash out at you or make you feel guilty for even thinking that they might be using Methamphetamine. They may storm off in an attempt to avoid discussing the issue. They may list reasons that they have not to use Methamphetamine as a logical way to convince you that they aren't. They may tell you that there is no way they are using Methamphetamine because they are holding a full time job or say they would never use because they wouldn't do that to their children or to you. They may tell you there is no way they can be using because they passed a drug screen at work or are not loosing any weight. They are attempting to turn the conversation around and make you second guess yourself or make you feel guilty that you thought that they "are a Meth addict."

I have heard so many times from parents that their child's reaction was along the lines of, "I can't believe that you think I am using Methamphetamine," or "You don't love or trust me?"

The fact that they are not willing to admit their use is often frustrating and arguments usually result from that. Remember that you are not dealing with your loved one in a right frame of mind. Everything is upside down and you can expect the opposite from them of how you thought they might act. Remain calm and force yourself not to argue with them or become upset or angry.

When I am teaching someone how to approach a Methamphetamine user, I often give them the following advice. First, keep a social distance and don't try to touch them or physically get close to them. They do not want contact from anyone other than maybe another user and they certainly don't want someone closing in on their social space. Second, slow your speech and lower the tone of your voice. Speak to them like you would a child. Not condescending, just clearly and quietly. Lastly, keep them talking and try to maintain eye contact. It is hard for a user to look someone directly in the eyes, but ask for them to look at you so they know that you are being genuine and honest with them.

If they disassociate from you, then you are probably not getting through. Make sure that you stick to you guns, but don't press them into running away. Be prepared to have some ultimatums ready and let them know how dedicated you are to helping them help themselves. Consider making the suggestion that they talk about their problem with someone else. I have seen many young Methamphetamine users that were a lot more willing to discuss their problems with me than with their parents. Be willing to leave the intervention if you sense that your loved one does not want to talk with you in the room.

You may consider the contact that you made at the police department as the person that helps you with the intervention. The one concern if you are using a law enforcement officer is that you make sure that they are not in uniform while they are around your loved one. You may have to specifically request them not to wear their uniform and explain to them why you are making that request. Uniforms make Methamphetamine users very uncomfortable.

Whomever you decide to help you with confronting your loved one, make sure that you spend the time prior to the meeting going over your situation and what you have been noticing that led you to believe that there is a problem. In the end no matter how much you have prepared and no matter how good your intentions are, expect it not to go the way that you want it to.

K   *Know that you are doing the right thing by being involved.*

To repeat, it is better to be involved in your loved ones treatment than be forced into getting their last affairs in order. Even if you are wrong about their use, they should be willing to see that you were doing it for the right reasons. More times than not though, you are right about their use and you are right about being involved. Not getting involved is the same to me as letting your loved one stand in the middle of a road and watch them get run over by a bus. We are talking about just as grave a situation.

L   *Let your loved one know that you do love them and that you are willing to do anything in your power to help them with their problem except ignore it.*

Explain to them that you are there for them as long as they are willing to be there for themselves. It is hard for a user to understand love because of the chemical changes that are going on in their body, but many times all they want to hear from someone is that they are loved. Explain to them that everything that you are doing, have done or will do is motivated by love and that you are not just picking on them or trying to run their life.

M   *Make them realize that you know there is a problem.*

Tell them the things that you see about their life that caused you concern. Ask them to explain the signs and symptoms you see and tell them you can't be fooled by the excuses they give for them. Repeat to them the excuses they gave for the signs you are seeing, because if something does not make sense to you then it might make them see how foolish what they are saying sounds. If they see you realize there is a problem and you are dealing with them having a Methamphetamine problem, then maybe they will be willing to start dealing with it. Tell them you know they are using the drug if you relatively sure that they are and keep telling them that you know it until they are willing to be honest with themselves.

N   *Never allow them an out to quitting.*

Be relentless in your efforts. If you have your mind set that you are going to make sure they get help, and then make sure that is exactly what happens. If they say they are willing to get treatment, then you take them immediately to a treatment facility. If they say they are going to move out of a house or apartment where there is Methamphetamine being used, then you show up and help them move. If they say they are going to quit using, then you make sure that you have the checks and balances in place to ensure that they have quit.

As an example, you can purchase your own urinalysis exams at major retailers or you could contact a local lab to see if they will take hair samples and use that to test for their use. If they say they are trying to get away from the drug, then that also means they have to get away from drug using friends. Make sure that they don't hang out with this crowd.

A recovering Methamphetamine user with three weeks of treatment under their belt is not mentally or physically well enough to help a friend quit using Methamphetamine. Users that have recently quit are just as excited as anyone to help others that they know that are still using Methamphetamine quit using as well. I have heard many people new in their recovery say that they and a current user are "going to do it together". The only thing that Meth users can do together is use Meth. If they say that they called a treatment provider or hospital looking for help, then make them prove where or whom they called. If they say they are going to a certain person's house, then go by there and make sure that is where they are.

If they say they are driving to the store then you ride with them. I have heard parents say that the user went out for gas or milk and eventually come back days later. Make them prove to you that they are going to treatment groups by having the group leader sign and date a sheet of paper. Take the time to make the user understands that it is not that you don't trust them. Even if you don't, you are acting as their accountability partner as far as their use in concerned. Please understand that their Methamphetamine using friends are going to be relentless in keeping them on the drug, so you will have to be even more vigilant in your efforts. They may hate you forever for being so pushy, but at least they will be alive to hate you.

O   *O*pen your home to them.

If the situation requires or if it becomes necessary to aid in getting someone help, you may consider moving your loved one into your home to provide them a place to stay that is separate from their Methamphetamine use. Many users are in need of a place that is not a constant temptation. I have seen loved ones open their home for their children, cousins, friends, and even for their own mom or dad to use as a haven for them to begin getting better. Make sure that you set rules before you agree to let them stay and stress that those rules are nonnegotiable.

You may consider that treatment is a stipulation for them coming into your home and as long as they are in treatment, then they are welcome in your home. Setting curfews may be an option or not allowing them to go out with their friends at all until they get better may be a rule you want to establish. It may be something just as simple as them having to be honest with you all the time. Obviously their having Methamphetamine in the house for any reason is never an option. Make sure you are clear on the rules and what the expectations are. Stick to your decision to take action if one of the rules is broken.

Before you consider taking anyone that is a drug user into your home, you should realize you put yourself at risk for law enforcement interaction. Arguments and fighting may result in the need for you to call the police. Before you let any user into your home this may be the time to let your contact at the police department know that you are moving the user into your home, so that if there is a problem down the line, there is someone at the police department familiar with the situation.

Take every situation into consideration. Don't let your generosity lead you into a bad place by allowing the user to take your car, have information on your bank records or unlimited access to your telephone service. Imagine what the user could do if allowed free reign to abuse you. If you feel led to provide them a place to stay after you have considered the possibilities then you are probably doing the right thing.

Many times a user needs a place to hide from other users, they need a place to sleep and they need a quiet place to get their head on straight. Many users advanced in their use have run out of money, food, friends or a place to lay their head. This despondency may be what is keeping them discouraged into not quitting or seeing a reason to quit.

P   *Put them out of your house if need be.*

If the loved one currently lives with you or you have allowed them into your home but they are not willing to make an effort to stop their use, they need to leave. The fact that a user may need a place to stay is mirrored by the opposite, and having a place to stay may be what provides them with enough reason not to quit. I know that this may not make sense, but many users will hold onto anything that they can to avoid quitting. Reaching the end of their rope may be the only reason that they find for quitting.

There is a scripture in the King James Bible in I Corinthians 5:5 that states, "To deliver such an one unto Satan for the destruction of the flesh, that the spirit may be saved in the day of our Lord Jesus." I think this to mean that in some cases you have to turn someone over to their wrong doing in order for them to find the end of their rope. Only then do they look for help. When you are dealing with someone that refuses to stop destructive behavior you should not try to prevent their destructive behavior but allow them to take the road that they have chosen. If you put off the inevitable (reaching the bottom of the barrel), you are only doing just that. That is putting off the inevitable. Sometimes it might be best not to postpone their fall into desperation because you are also postponing their treatment and recovery. I have talked with many users who told me that as long as they had a little money in their pocket or a roof over their head, they had not gotten to the bottom of the barrel and therefore had no reason to stop using.

Of course, as I said before, there might be criminal problems that arise as a result of someone's using or distributing Methamphetamine at your residence. It might be a good idea to contact an attorney, the police or the appropriate court to discuss the legality of forcing someone out of your home. Going through the legal and proper procedure covers you if there is a problem with the police.

Also, you might consider changing your locks or security codes on alarm systems after they have left. I have seen many users break into prior residences to steal or cause trouble after they have left. You hate to think that your loved one might steal from you, but you might be an easy target, especially parents, for cash, jewelry or credit card thefts. Just try not to do

anything that helps or aids in allowing your loved one to continue their use.

Q Quitting is the only option.

As you make a decision on allowing someone into your home or if you are planning on kicking them out of your house, the constant truth is that their quitting is the only option. Help the person think of all the reasons that they have for quitting the Meth use. Write down the things you can think of so when the time comes and you hear the question, "Why should I quit?" or you hear "I can't stop using!" you have something to offer.

Often users will find one thing that is their constant goal or motivation for not using. It might be their children or their marriage or they might be doing it just for themselves. Find out what that one thing is and constantly remind them of their motivation. Encourage them that they can stop using because other people just like them have stopped. Remind them that you will be there for them as long as quitting is always the goal. Now they may slip and use again which might cause for tension, but quitting must remain the goal.

R Report them to the police.

If your loved one refuses help, it may be a good idea to turn over any information you have gained to the police to assist in having them arrested for their illegal activity. In the past, I felt that arresting someone was the only way to correct their behavior. With Methamphetamine use, I realized that treatment was an important part in getting someone well and that jail time was not going to cure them from the sickness of addiction.

But with Meth, I also realized being arrested might be the only thing that breaks that downward spiral. It might be the one thing that stops them long enough to look at themselves and realize how bad they have gotten. In most cases where someone completely refuses help, I suggest to the loved one that they report the abuser to the police.

There are just too many problems they can find themselves in if they don't stop their use, and getting arrested and sitting in jail is often better than watching them die or kill someone else. The reality of an overdose is a real possibility and one that may be mitigated if the user is in jail. Also, no one thinks that their loved one would ever commit some terrible act of violence, but there is always that chance while Meth is in the picture. Murder, robbery, child abuse and neglect are all too common when someone is on Methamphetamine.

You can use all the things that you learned in the "G" portion of this book to report their activity to law enforcement. I would always suggest that you remain anonymous when reporting a loved one to law enforcement or get the officer's reassurance that what you tell them will remain anonymous. I would also resist the temptation of telling your loved one that you called the police on them. Generally an outburst like this is most common during an argument. They will remember that you said you called the police. Even if you aren't the reason that they were arrested, they will blame you for it. Many times though they might thank you for it.

During my career, I was rarely thanked for doing my job, particularly when it came to putting someone in jail. With Methamphetamine, I am often thanked by the person that I arrested because it was the thing they needed to get them back on the right course. I have even received a letter or two from an inmate relaying thanks to me for putting them there instead of a cemetery somewhere.

Of course you aren't trying to put them in prison for years and years, you are only trying to get them in jail long enough to let them realize that they need help. But realize you reporting them to law enforcement and it might have serious consequences, potentially even resulting in a prison stay. Often many users will seek treatment to avoid a long-term stint and a judge will usually consider treatment options versus long prison terms.

Any reason that a user decides to seek treatment is a good reason. Stop for a minute and think about this option. This seems to be the hardest step for someone to take, especially a parent, and rightfully so, because it seems so opposite to what you should do for your child. I think it also seems like you are betraying your loved one and that is a hard thing to get past. Most aren't willing to take this step until after many months of dealing with the user. I believe you will know when the time is right to take this action.

The biggest thing to remember is that when you do take this step and your loved one finds themselves in jail, don't bond them out hours after they are arrested. Many days or weeks might be needed before the user realizes their need for help. I would suggest that you visit them as often as you can while they are in jail and watch their attitude change. Don't let them put the guilt trip on you. Remember that no one wants to be in jail.

If you get to this point, it might be a good time to retry or, to try for the first time, to confront them about their use. Only help them if they are willing to talk about their use and do something about the problem. I have seen many parents who have agreed to bond their child out of jail and right into a treatment facility. If you both agree to do this, go straight to the treatment facility. If you don't, there's a good chance they'll disappear right back into the Methamphetamine world that you are so desperately trying get them out of.

S   *Stop all means of support that you are providing.*

If you are in a situation where you find yourself supporting the user because of a certain circumstance, then you have to make a decision if you are going to continue that support. Most commonly I see this in the parent/college student type setting or in circumstances where the family might by wealthy. I remember a phone call I took from a concerned mother who explained to me that her daughter had just been arrested in Florida for manufacturing Methamphetamine in the house that she and her husband had provided her to live in. It appeared that the daughter moved to Florida to work as a marine biologist and they allowed her to move into their summer home. The parents received a call one day from their daughter that she was quitting her job and was going to work in a tattoo parlor. Shortly thereafter she was arrested on the Meth charges and for being in possession of a lab in their summer home. My advice to them was to sell the house immediately, stop all means of support that and move her back to Georgia if the judge in Florida would give her a bond.

Now your situation might not be as dramatic as the one I just mentioned, but you might be providing support to someone in some way or another that is helping them along in their use. Cell phones are always a big concern of mine. I attribute teenage drug use in a small part to the technology that our young kids are provided. With them, there is instant access to a network of youth the minute they are handed a cell phone, a network that includes drug users and drug dealers. The internet has the same potential in that many Methamphetamine users will talk and arrange drug transactions via email.

Many parents also provide their children with vehicles and pay the insurance, inadvertently providing them with the means to go and participate in their drug use. Now, I'm not saying that providing them these things is a bad thing. I am just making you aware of how they can be abused. I suggest that you take away all means of support. If there is a cell phone in your name, turn it off. If there is a vehicle in your name, take it back and cancel the insurance. Any form of financial support should be suspended. I would explain to your loved one that as long as they are continuing their destructive behavior, will not participate by giving them things that they might use to further their problem.

T *Talk to them, talk to them, talk to them.*

Make sure you talk to them every time you can. I don't necessarily mean that you need to talk to them as often as you can about their Methamphetamine use, just talk to them as often as you can about all that you can. We learned in this book that many users isolate themselves from everyone in their life especially their loved ones as a result of their use. Hiding from you is a good way to hide the problem. Reaching out to them about everything that is going on in their life might be a way to bring them out of hiding. The more that you know about their life and their daily activities, the harder it will be for them to fall away back into their hiding place.

Be upfront and honest and tell them your concerns. You should tell them what you are doing and why you are doing it. Honesty, as much as is practical, is always the best policy. I know that when you are dealing with someone breaking the law and willing to lie, cheat and steal to use the drug, honesty is not always possible. Just remember that Meth users are able to spot or root out a lie very well because it is what they are good at. Often getting caught in a lie is a major setback, but having an open line of communication to explain your actions might help.

You can open a new line of communication by leaving them messages on their voicemail, by writing them a letter or emailing if you can. The important thing is to keep a dialogue going with them. Make an agreement with them from the start that no matter what happens you will keep talking. It is better to talk and disagree than it is not to talk and have nothing to disagree about.

U   Understand what they are going through.

Wear their shoes for a few minutes. I'm not trying to be the bleeding heart everyone thinks I am, and I definitely am not saying I want you to justify something I think is wrong. I am not asking you to make excuses for what they are doing or the trouble that they've gotten themselves into. What I am saying is that there is a reason why your loved one used Methamphetamine for the first time and you might be a part of that reason.

Kids from homes where their parent used drugs, children from broken homes or spouses trying to escape a troubled marriage are some of the most common reasons I hear. Try to set aside your differences and see there are issues they are dealing with other than their Methamphetamine itself. Be willing to walk with them in this problem and be open to requests they have within reason. They might want you to go to counseling with them, they might want you to go with them to a group treatment meeting, or they might just want you to be with them to go to church in search of a spiritual connection. If you love them, then share with them in their struggle instead of just looking in from the outside.

Think about what you would be willing to do for something you had to have and how you might act if you ever used Methamphetamine. You might have never gotten to the point where you think you would steal or kill, but I bet you have already proven many of us have done something that was not smart to get something we wanted. Understanding the ins and outs of why your loved one used Methamphetamine may make you understand them better as a person. For you, quitting Methamphetamine seems to be a simple decision to make and it makes all the sense in the world, but from their eyes it isn't simple.

Understand that their need for the drug is just as strong a desire as the one you have for breathing. They have to have it, and just admitting there is a problem means that they may have to quit something they have their strongest desires for. Understanding this need might help you realize why they do the things they do and might make you realize they really aren't the horrible person that they've become. Just try to take a different perspective on things and remain open to them when the time comes.

V   View your progress as progress and view your failures as progress.

It is easy to call the good things that happen a success and to get excited about them, but it is hard to feel encouraged or feel as if you are winning a battle when failures come along so often. I have met parents that have told me they want to help with the Methamphetamine problem because they lost their son or daughter to the drug. I assumed they meant that their son or daughter died as a result of Meth use. In reality, what I found out was they had just written them off because they were lost to the drug. I say that as long as they are alive, you can be doing something to help them, even if it is just a prayer. Sometimes you will find that spiritual involvement is more beneficial than other forms of intervention. The point is, I want you to say you are doing something, because doing something that didn't work is always better than doing nothing at all. If you find that everything you are trying is not working, at least you are being successful in trying. Instead of looking at failed treatment options as failures look at them as one more treatment option you know didn't work, and that you're one treatment option closer to finding the one that will work.

I truly believe we are allowed to go through trials and tribulations so that we can help others as they walk through the same trials. I also believe that everything happens for a reason. Making notes and keeping up with what does not work for you in your situation might be a way for you to help someone get on the fast track to recovery. That failure, as you see it, might just be the beginnings of a success for someone else. Even if your loved one does not make it in their struggle with Methamphetamine use and they pass on, you will have some comfort in knowing you did all you could and used all that you had in your power to help them. If I am ever put in the situation you are in now, I would want to be able to look back when it was all over and say that I can sleep well at night knowing that I did everything in my power to help them.

W *Wait and see if they give in to accepting help and move forward or start over.*

As you press them towards getting treatment, always be willing and ready to hear the word, "okay." You never know when it might happen, but hopefully sooner or later it will. Don't be in such a hurry for them to get their life turned around overnight. Getting to the point that they admit that there is a problem is a huge accomplishment and in certain situations you might need to just sit and watch to make sure that the signs and symptoms are going away and that they are doing their part to get the problem taken care of.

Don't press them as long as you see that they are doing the right thing. You should watch to see if they are keeping their treatment appointments, wait to see if they are putting on weight or if they are eating and sleeping right. It's basically waiting to see if their lives get back on track. By saying this, I don't want you to think that I want you to lay off being involved; I am only saying that you might consider easing off how hard you are pressing them to get help if it appears that they are. Become more supportive and encouraging instead of nagging and aggressive. I have seen many people press their loves ones so hard and never stop to encourage and congratulate the user as they are making successful steps towards getting better. I guess they are so keyed in on the way that their loved one used to act, that they don't believe what they are hearing. It's kind of like not believing chicken little that the sky is falling, because with Methamphetamine use, you may be tired of hearing the lies. If they earn a little trust then give them a little trust. I have talked to addicts who fell back into using because they had been so unbelievable while they were using that they found it hard for anyone to believe in them when they weren't.

Once the ball is rolling with treatment and they have expressed their desire to get help, then you can slow down a little and wait to see how things are going. This is the time to back off, watch, wait and allow the treatment providers, counselors or law enforcement officers do what it is that they are paid to do. Many parents get so excited and wrapped up about being involved they don't know how to just sit back and relax. On the other hand, if you are watching and waiting and nothing is happening, then start back over on the step where things might have gone wrong or reconsider a fresh approach.

$X + Y = Z$

There is no magic or perfect formula I can give you that will work in every situation. I wish I could give you a simple solution to a complex problem. I wish there were some way that you could easily get someone away from the grips of Meth as easily as it was for them to get wrapped up in their addiction. The truth is that it is so easy to pick up Meth and use it for the first time and nearly impossible to put it down.

Every Methamphetamine related incident, problem or intervention that I am a part of is constantly changing and always different from the next situation I might encounter. Every story has its own twist and each has to be looked at on a one by one basis. While they are all unique in some way, the basic problem is always the same and the tragic stories are all similar. The drug is the same and what it does to users is constant and definite. That is why combating the drug can be a constant as well. That is why I think if you use this book it will help. I believe this book is a guide to the Methamphetamine problem as a whole, and I think it is a valuable tool. Just like any tool, it is not what brings success to the situation it is the individual using the tool who wields it to success. I want you to be aware that you may have to try several approaches to the problem to be successful. You might have to rethink things and change your plan right in the middle of this book. Be flexible and be willing to try things that you would not normally try.

I want you to use this book as if it were a weapon against this drug, because you are truly in a fight against all that is evil. Meth is a drug that alters people's minds and bodies in a way that they are going to react differently than you might expect. Always expect the unexpected and prepare for the worst so that you're as prepared as you can be. Remember that you are not dealing with your loved one on Methamphetamine; you are dealing with the drug itself. Don't keep information to yourself do get involved in that person's life as soon as you can because that might save their life.

I can't stress the question enough, "If you don't do something to help them, then who will?" God bless you in your efforts as you go and I pray that you will be able to turn the key and release someone from Methamphetamine's prison.

- The End -

Ice Methamphetamine

Ice Methamphetamine in jeweler's bag

Ice or Meth Pipe

Ice or Meth Pipe

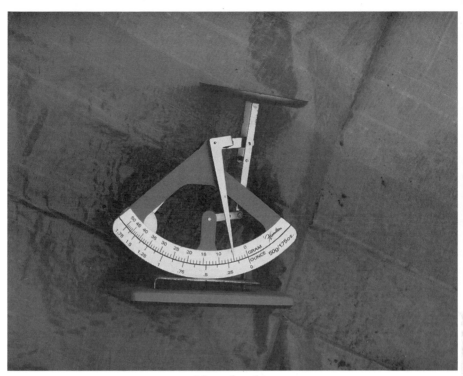

Manual scales

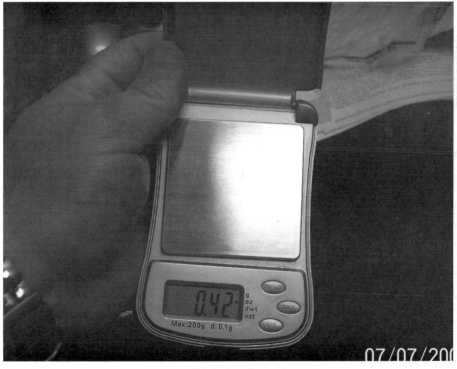

Digital scales

Light bulb converted to Meth pipe

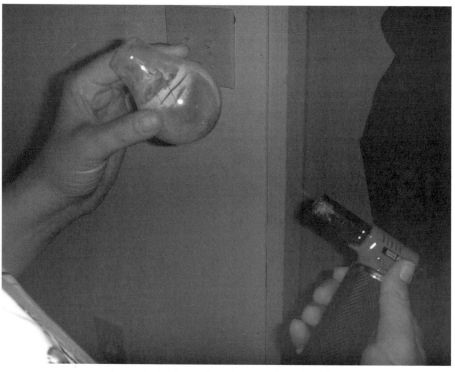

Converted light bulb and propane style lighter

Propane lighter used to smoke Methamphetamine

Methamphetamine in jeweler's bags

Methamphetamine crystals or "shards"

6 ounces of Ice Methamphetamine

<u>Notes</u>

The following pages are designed to act as a workbook or notebook for you to write your observations, thoughts, and research. Not every letter in the ABC's of the intervention portion of this book will have a page for notes. The pages that are provided contain practical thoughts to guide you in developing your plan.

A   <u>Acknowledge that there might be a problem.</u>

Use this page as a check list for the symptoms that you have seen or see now that lead you to believe there is a problem.

   ___   Irritability and aggressive behavior
   ___   Anxiety, stress, and nervousness
   ___   Auditory or visual hallucinations
   ___   Paranoia or feelings of plotting or conspiracy
   ___   Long periods of being awake
   ___   Long periods of catatonic like sleep
   ___   Extreme weight loss or decreased appetite
   ___   Extreme dehydration
   ___   Sores on the arms, neck, or face
   ___   Dilated Pupils
   ___   Overall rough or careless appearance
   ___   Bad teeth, dirty hands and nails
   ___   Obsessive behavior
   ___   Increased sexuality or talk of sex
   ___   Drug related paraphernalia
   ___   Lack of focus and constant change in conversation
   ___   Profuse sweating
   ___   Increased alertness or hyperactivity
   ___   Staying up all night and sleeping all day
   ___   Mood swings from extreme to extreme

B   <u>Begin to accept that there is a problem.</u>

List any reasons why you think that your loved one might have started using Methamphetamine.

C   <u>Choose to do something about the problem.</u>

You are deciding to do something about the problem and you must commit to helping your loved one in any way that you can. Take the time to reiterate to yourself and with anyone that has agreed to help you with this endeavor that you are willing to do something about the problem and then sign the line(s) below. By signing you are committing to yourself and to your loved one that you are willing to do what it takes to help release them from the chains of addiction.

Signed: _____

Signed: _____

Signed: _____

Signed: _____

Signed: _____

D   <u>Develop a plan of action.</u>

List on this page any thoughts that you have initially about what direction you might take concerning your loved one.

_____
_____
_____
_____
_____
_____
_____
_____
_____
_____
_____
_____
_____
_____
_____
_____

E   <u>Enlist help wherever you can from people that are willing to assist you in developing your plan.</u>

List on this page anyone that you have contacted or could contact that might be able to help you in your situation.

<u>Name</u>	<u>Phone</u>	<u>Email</u>

F

Find out what has worked for other concerning their problem with Methamphetamine.

List on this page any names, numbers, email addresses, or websites of programs that have helped other people dealing with Methamphetamine addiction.

_____
_____
_____
_____
_____
_____
_____
_____
_____
_____
_____
_____
_____
_____
_____
_____
_____

G

Get all the information that you can that is specific to your situation.

What do you know or what have you learned about your loved one's Methamphetamine use?

_____
_____
_____
_____
_____
_____
_____
_____
_____
_____
_____
_____

H   <u>Have several treatment options ready to go.</u>

Take time to research the options that you have available to you concerning treatment and make your notes here.

_____
_____
_____
_____
_____
_____
_____
_____
_____
_____
_____
_____
_____
_____
_____
_____
_____
_____

I   <u>Initiate your plan into action.</u>

What ideas do you have about initiating your plan into action?

_____
_____
_____
_____
_____
_____
_____
_____
_____
_____
_____
_____
_____
_____

J   Just expect the worse in your reaction and theirs.

K   Know that you are doing the right thing by being involved.

L   Let your loved one know that you love them and that you are willing to do anything to help them with their problem except ignore it.

M   Make them realize that you know there is a problem.

N   Never give them an out.

O   Open your home to them.

P   Put them out of your home.

Q   Quitting is the only option.

R   Report them to the police.

If you have gotten to this point and you have decided to report your loved on to a law enforcement agency it is important that you realize you are going to provide information to a law enforcement agency for the purpose of them making an arrest on your loved one. Once this course of action has been set in motion it may be irreversible. Make sure that you have made this decision after careful consideration and with the belief that nothing else will work to get their attention.

Agency	Contact Person	Telephone Number

S   Stop all means of support that you are providing.

What means of support have you been providing that has enabled your loved one to continue their Methamphetamine use?

T Talk to them, talk to them, talk to them.

U Understand what they are going through.

V View your progress as progress and your failures as progress.

W Wait and see if they give in to accepting help and move forward or start over.

X+Y=Z